Mechanical Advantage and Efficiency

Authors
Carol Glegg
Peter Williams

Program Consultant
Marietta (Mars) Bloch

Nelson
Thomson Learning™

Australia • Canada • Denmark • Japan • Mexico • New Zealand • Philippines
Puerto Rico • Singapore • South Africa • Spain • United Kingdom • United States

Contents

Unit 3 Overview

M achines make it easier for us to do things. Designers and engineers are constantly tinkering, planning, and testing to create the most efficient machines and products. What makes them efficient? The efficiency of machines and products can be measured in many ways: by how much energy they use; by how easy they are to use or operate; and, increasingly, by the impact they have on our environment.

Mechanisms and Efficiency

Different mechanisms give different outputs for the same energy input. The choice of mechanisms affects the efficiency of a machine.

You will be able to:

- measure the mechanical advantage and velocity ratio of simple mechanisms

- understand how enclosed liquids and gases transmit and magnify a force, and how this is different from the way solids behave

- predict the mechanical advantage of different mechanisms before measuring the effects of friction

- calculate pressure and describe its effects on hydraulic and pneumatic systems

- recognize how friction affects a machine's efficiency and examine ways to reduce friction

- design and build a mechanical system that is operated by a hydraulic or pneumatic system

Efficient Systems

Each part in the system plays a role in the efficient operation of a machine.

You will be able to:

- explore the differences between an enclosed liquid (hydraulic) system and a gas (pneumatic) system

- describe how hydraulic and pneumatic systems are used

- understand the different uses of simple machines such as levers and gears in designing mechanisms

- design and build systems involving linkages, pulley systems, and winches

Designing and Building Efficient Products

To design the best product, designers and engineers must keep in mind the needs of the user, the needs of society, and the needs of the environment.

You will be able to:

- explore the personal and societal factors that determine whether a product is used

- analyze designs of products for their ability to meet diverse human needs

- test key features of products and analyze test results

- propose modifications to improve the quality of products

- design and build efficient, user-friendly products and machines

- assess the environmental impact resulting from the manufacture, use, and disposal of a variety of products

- explore how the design and efficient use of machines is related to people's ability to use them knowledgeably, safely, and comfortably

Design Challenge

You will be able to ...
demonstrate your learning by completing a Design Challenge.

An Efficient Device or Model Machine

Every machine begins as an idea. Then, careful planning, design, and calculations are necessary to build the most appropriate, efficient model that is durable, user-friendly, and environmentally friendly.

In this unit you will be able to design and build:

1 **A Can Crusher**
Design and build a device that people can use to easily crush their cans before depositing them in public recycling bins.

2 **A Windmill-Operated Water Well**
Design and build a model of a water well that is powered by the wind.

3 **A Remote-Control Puppet**
Design and build a puppet whose limbs are moved remotely through a hydraulic or pneumatic system.

To start your Design Challenge, see page 54.

Record your thoughts and design ideas for the Challenge when you see:

Design Challenge

Getting Started

Using Machines to Get Things Done

1 Mechanisms, which are made from simple machines like levers and pulleys, are built into both large and small devices. These devices allow people to pull, push, or lift objects, often without applying much force. How can you tell which mechanisms will be most effective? How do you measure or predict how much force will be needed to operate the machine? What effect does friction have on the efficiency of a mechanism?

2 Mechanical, hydraulic (liquid), and pneumatic (gas) systems are everywhere, but we rarely notice them. From garbage trucks to dentists' drills, these systems can change the direction or speed of movement or multiply or transfer force to lift or push things. How do these systems work? How can we make them more useful and more efficient?

3 Machines and other products must be designed and made with the consumer and the environment in mind. How can the designers know that the product will be easy to use, safe, and reliable? In the chain from design to disposal, where will the product affect the environment? How can that impact be reduced?

Reflecting

Think about the questions in **1**,**2**,**3**. What other questions do you have about mechanical advantage and efficiency? As you progress through this unit, reflect on your answers and revise them based on what you have learned.

Try This The Can Opener: A Simple Device

We use can openers almost every day without much thought. But try opening a can without one!

- Take a close look at a hand-powered can opener.

1. Can openers open cans in a two-step process. What are the two steps?

2. For each step, explain what happens when a force is applied. Draw diagrams showing the direction of the force in each step.

- Try to use the can opener by pressing on the handles near its joint.

3. (a) Is it easier or harder to use?

(b) Would it be easier or harder if the handles were longer? Why?

- Try to turn the handle with your fingers at the centre of the handle.

4. Is it easier or harder to wind the handle?

5. What is the purpose of the round, toothed part of the can opener?

6. Do you think the metal of the can opener is stronger than the metal of the can? What evidence do you have that supports your conclusion?

7. What modifications might make a can opener easier to use?

Designing Machines

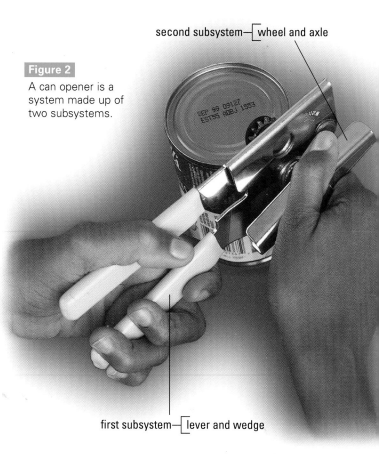

The can opener has essentially remained the same since it was patented in 1858 (**Figure 1**). Why has this machine endured in its design over so many years? Many attempts at different designs have shown us that this design is the most efficient to date: no one has yet found an easier way to open a can (unless you use electricity!).

Machines are designed to help make things easier for us to do. They meet a specific need or perform a task. A **machine** can
- transform energy;
- transfer forces from one place to another;
- change the direction of a force;
- change the magnitude of a force; and/or
- increase or decrease speed.

Machines as Systems

Most machines can be thought of as a system made up of subsystems. Each subsystem performs a different function; together they make up a system that performs a certain task or larger function. The typical can opener has two subsystems (**Figure 2**). The first subsystem, made up of a lever and a wedge, is designed to pierce and cut the metal of the lid. The second subsystem, made up of a wheel and axle, rotates the can.

Many subsystems are made up of mechanisms. A **mechanism** is a system of moving parts that changes an input motion and force into a desired output motion and force (**Figure 3**). Most machines have their mechanisms hidden from view within the body of the machine. Although we rarely see these subsystems, we can be sure that wherever movement takes place—whether in a simple device like a can opener or in a complex technological system like the Canadarm on the space shuttle (**Figure 4**)— mechanisms will be found.

Figure 1

The invention of the can opener was a response to the use of cans for storing food. Its function is to remove the lid of a can safely.

second subsystem—⌐ wheel and axle

Figure 2

A can opener is a system made up of two subsystems.

first subsystem—⌐ lever and wedge

Figure 3

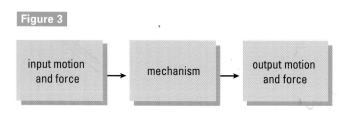

input motion and force → mechanism → output motion and force

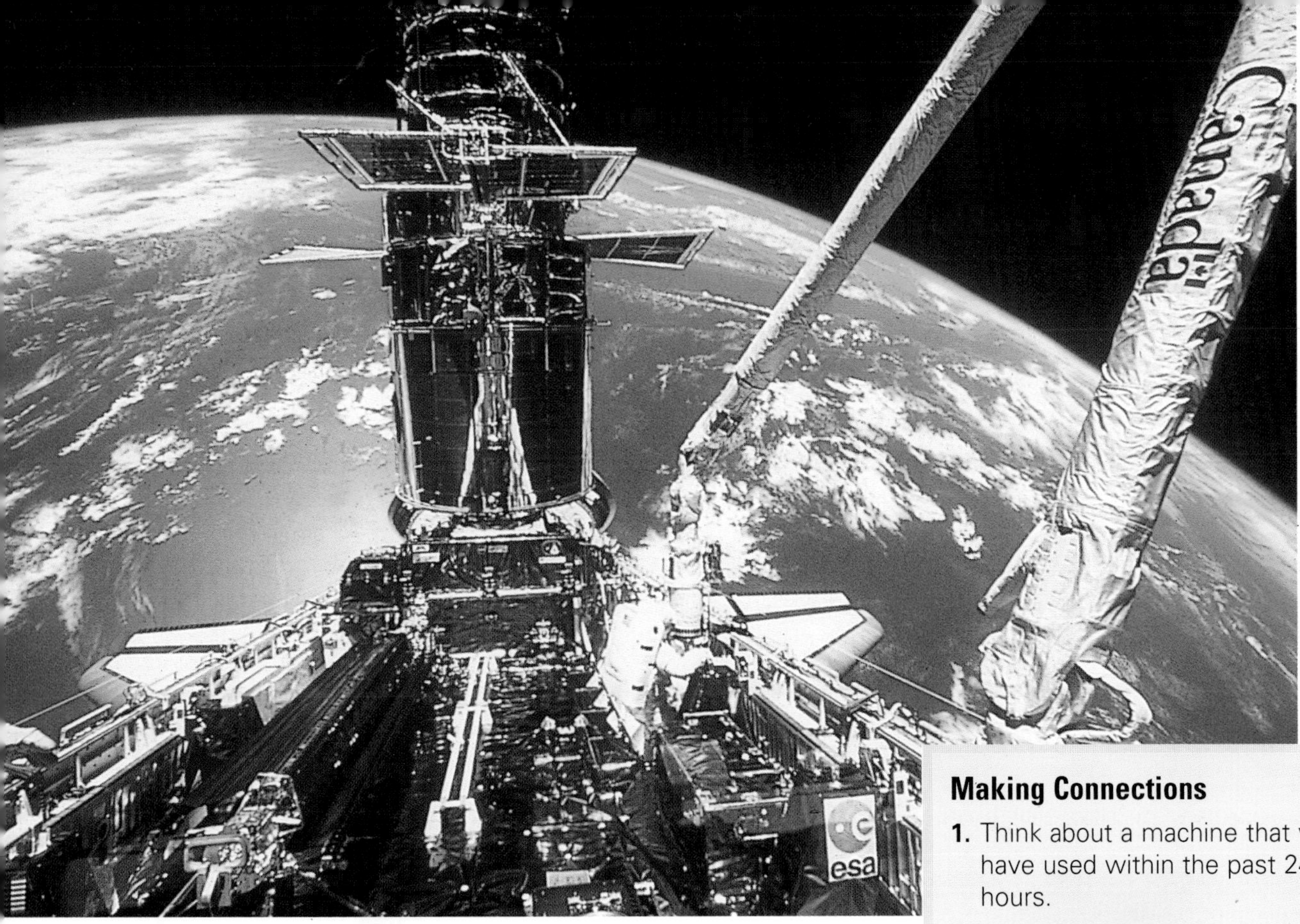

Figure 4

Machines and Controls

The can opener, and any other system, can only operate as a system if each subsystem performs its function, works together with the other subsystems, and has an energy supply. There is one more requirement: control. Think about opening a can. A can can be opened slowly or quickly. Some cans are harder to open than others—more force is needed—but sometimes only until the can is "started." Sometimes the opener gets "stuck" or the subsystem that rotates the can hasn't got a good grip—the opener must be taken off the can, and reapplied. The human operator controls both the can opener and the movement of the can using the grip (the lever) by changing the magnitude of the force applied and by changing the point of application of the opener. If there is no human operator controlling every force, a machine must have its own internal controls: a way of varying the force applied, the speed of the operation, and so on. To work efficiently and reliably without human intervention, a machine's controls must be **self-correcting**—they must adjust to the situation. More complicated machines usually require more complicated controls.

Making Connections

1. Think about a machine that you have used within the past 24 hours.
   - (a) How was the machine useful to you?
   - (b) Identify the subsystems in the machine and their functions.
   - (c) Summarize how the subsystems contribute to the overall purpose of the machine.
2. When a can opener is being operated, what are the input motion and force? The output motion and force?

Exploring

3. (8B) Using electronic and print sources, research what types of materials have been added to make can openers easier or more comfortable to operate. Prepare a poster with a diagram showing how different parts of the basic structure of the can opener have been modified over time.

Reflecting

4. (8D) Write a short story describing what your life might be like if society had not developed machines.

SKILLS HANDBOOK: (8B) Creating a Design Folder (8D) Exploring an Issue

Levers: How They Work

When you swing a baseball bat or use a shovel you are using a lever. A lever is a rigid bar that pivots at a point called a fulcrum. Levers can multiply a small force into a large force. When you are digging a hole with a shovel, the input (effort) force is multiplied into a larger output (load) force, and you are able to move a heavy load of soil.

Types of Levers

Levers are found in all sorts of tools and in complex machines such as cranes and robots. Despite this variety, there are only three types of levers: Class 1, Class 2, and Class 3. Each classification is based on the relative positions of the effort, fulcrum, and load. Choosing which type of lever to use in a design depends on the input motion and force and what output motion and force is desired.

A Class 1 lever can move a heavy load with a small force. In a Class 1 lever, the fulcrum is between the load force and the effort force. The **load force** is the force exerted by the load, and the **effort force** is the force required to move the load. An example of a Class 1 lever is a screwdriver being used to pry off the lid of a paint can. (See **Figure 1**.)

A Class 2 lever always moves a large load using a small effort force. Unlike in a Class 1 lever, here the fulcrum is at one end. The load acts between the effort and the fulcrum. A wheelbarrow (**Figure 2**) is an example of Class 2 levers.

Unlike Class 1 and 2 levers, Class 3 levers always make things harder to lift or move instead of easier. In a Class 3 lever the fulcrum is at one end and the effort is exerted between the load and the fulcrum. As a result, the load arm is always longer than the effort arm. A fishing rod (**Figure 3**) and a tennis racket are examples of Class 3 levers.

The chief advantage of Class 3 levers is that although a large effort is needed, the longer load arm can magnify movements.

load force

fulcrum

effort force = 250 N

fulcrum

load force = 750 N

load arm

effort arm

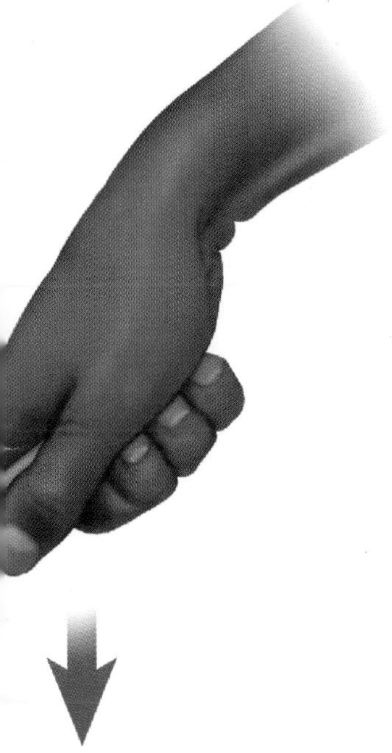

Mechanical Advantage

When designing machines it is helpful to know what benefit one mechanism provides compared to another. The usefulness of a mechanism can be expressed in quantitative terms. **Mechanical advantage** is the number of times by which a machine can increase or decrease the effort force. If you know the effort force and the load force, you can determine the mechanical advantage of the mechanism by calculating the following ratio:

$$\text{Mechanical Advantage (MA)} = \frac{\text{load force (N)}}{\text{effort force (N)}}$$

Mechanical advantage has no units. If the mechanical advantage of a machine is 1, the effort force is equal to the load force, and there is no advantage gained. If the mechanical advantage is less than 1, a large effort force is required to move a smaller load (as in Class 3 levers). Machines with a mechanical advantage greater than 1, as in Class 1 and Class 2 levers, allow larger loads to be moved with less effort.

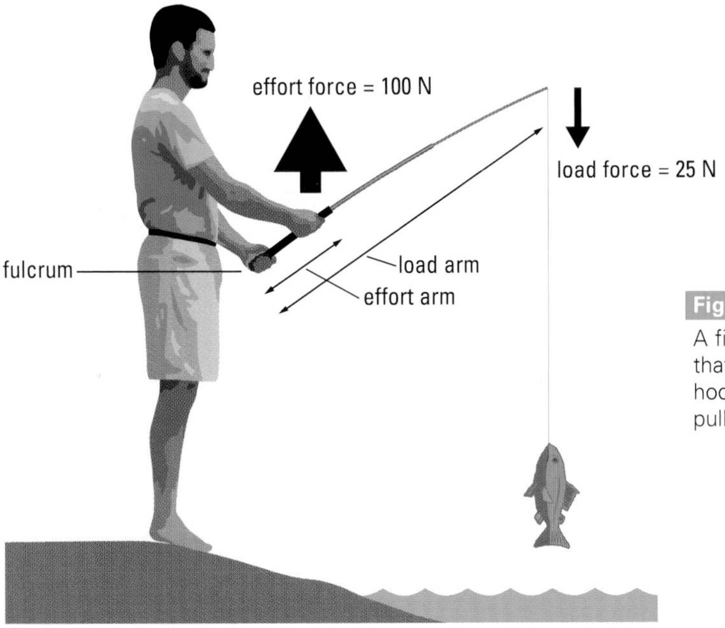

effort force

effort force = 100 N

load force = 25 N

fulcrum

load arm

effort arm

Figure 3

A fishing rod magnifies small wrist movements so that a person fishing can easily fling the fishing hook and line. However, a large force is needed to pull the fish out of the water.

Try This   Levering Advantage

- You can use the back of a chair, a metre stick, a newton scale, and a weight tied on a string to construct Class 1, 2, and 3 levers.

- Make an example of each class of lever. For each lever, use the newton scale to measure the effort force needed to lift the load.

- Draw a diagram of each lever. Label the fulcrum, load force, and effort force to lift the load.

1. For each lever, calculate the mechanical advantage.

- For each lever, try to improve the mechanical advantage.

2. What is the maximum mechanical advantage for each lever?

Mechanical Advantage and Levers

With levers the mechanical advantage is affected by the distance of the point of application of the load and effort forces from the fulcrum. This relationship is described in the following equation:

$$\text{Mechanical Advantage (MA)} = \frac{\text{length of effort arm}}{\text{length of load arm}}$$

This means that the mechanical advantage increases as the length of the effort arm increases, and also as the length of the load arm decreases.

You now have two ways to calculate mechanical advantage: you can use the measured lengths of the arms of the lever, or the measured magnitude of the forces, as shown in **Figure 4**.

In the real world, however, the two will not be equal. In **Figure 4** we simplified a little: in real life, friction would act on the painter's hand and the screwdriver as they move down, between the screwdriver and the can at the fulcrum, and on the screwdriver and the lid of the can as they move up. The mechanical advantage calculated using the length of the lever arms is useful *only for prediction without friction*. In application, the effort force that is needed will always be greater than the effort force you predict (based on the length of the lever arms) because it takes extra effort to overcome friction. To calculate the real mechanical advantage, you must measure forces.

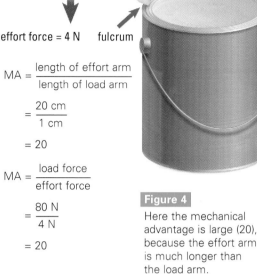

load force = 80 N

load arm = 1 cm

effort arm = 20 cm

effort force = 4 N   fulcrum

$$MA = \frac{\text{length of effort arm}}{\text{length of load arm}}$$

$$= \frac{20\ \text{cm}}{1\ \text{cm}}$$

$$= 20$$

$$MA = \frac{\text{load force}}{\text{effort force}}$$

$$= \frac{80\ \text{N}}{4\ \text{N}}$$

$$= 20$$

Figure 4
Here the mechanical advantage is large (20), because the effort arm is much longer than the load arm.

Velocity Ratio

If the mechanical advantage of a Class 3 lever is always less than 1, how can mechanisms using Class 3 levers still be useful? A tennis racket is an example of a Class 3 lever (**Figure 5**). Even though a large effort force is required to hit the ball, only a small wrist motion at the handle creates a large motion at the other end of the racket.

Therefore, if you compare the distance that the effort force moves with the distance the load force moves, you will see that, in a Class 3 lever, the load force moves farther than the effort force in the same length of time. The ratio of these two distances is called the **velocity ratio**. This is written as:

$$\text{Velocity Ratio} = \frac{\text{distance effort force moves}}{\text{distance load force moves}}$$

Like mechanical advantage, velocity ratio has no units.

For Class 3 levers, the velocity ratio is always less than 1. For Class 1 and 2 levers, the velocity ratio is larger than 1.

load distance

effort distance

Figure 5
Because the racket is a Class 3 lever, it takes a lot of effort to hit the ball over the net. However, the racket also multiplies small movements of the wrist, allowing the player to easily control the flight of the ball.

Efficient Lever Mechanisms

Levers are inexpensive and easy to use in the design of mechanisms, but how efficient are they in being able to move large loads for short distances? How can we determine how efficient a machine is?

You can calculate the efficiency of a mechanism by using the following ratio:

$$\text{Percentage efficiency} = \frac{\text{Mechanical Advantage}}{\text{Velocity Ratio}} \times 100$$

Without friction the percentage efficiency of levers is always 100%. However, in reality friction reduces the mechanical advantage of a lever, resulting in an efficiency that is less than 100%.

Connecting Levers Together

Many machines and other devices use a combination of levers called a linkage to transmit force and motion. A **linkage** is two or more levers connected together. The choice of where each fulcrum is placed affects the movement of the connecting lever(s). A given input motion and force can be transferred into the desired output motion and force. (See **Figure 6**.)

Figure 6

Linked levers can be found in a wide variety of mechanisms.

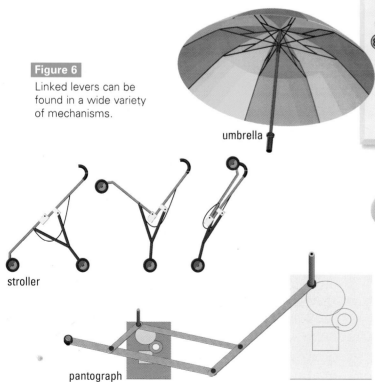

umbrella

stroller

pantograph

Understanding Concepts

1. (a) **6C** Draw diagrams of Class 1, 2, and 3 levers showing the fulcrum, load force, and effort force for each.

   (b) Give an explanation of each type.

   (c) Explain how Class 1 and 2 levers can make it easier and more efficient to move things.

2. (a) Define mechanical advantage.

   (b) What is the mechanical advantage of a lever in which the effort force required to move an object is 1/10 of the load force?

3. (a) Define velocity ratio.

   (b) How can you use mechanical advantage and velocity ratio to determine the efficiency of a lever?

Making Connections

4. (a) What type of lever is your arm? Your jaw?

   (b) Explain, using the length of effort arm, where the most powerful teeth in your mouth are located.

5. Mary is raking up wet, heavy leaves and moves her hands down the handle to make it shorter.

   (a) What type of lever is a rake?

   (b) Why will moving her hands make the raking easier?

Exploring

6. **8D** Many household products involve levers. Choose one that uses a lever and draw a diagram to show how it works by indicating the effort and load forces, the lengths of its effort and load arms, its power source, if any, and its materials. Be prepared to share your findings with the class.

Design Challenge

In designing your windmill-operated water well or can crusher, is it important to establish what the approximate mechanical advantage will be? If so, how will you decide what it should be?

3.3 Design Investigation

SKILLS MENU
○ Identify a Problem   ● Testing   ● Evaluating
● Planning   ● Recording   ● Communicating
● Building

Raise It Up

You have seen that linkage systems are part of many everyday products. One problem, when including levers in any machine or system, is getting them to fit into a limited amount of space, for example, inside a piano (**Figure 1**).

Problem

How can you create a compact system of linked levers to raise a weight a certain height?

Design Brief

Design and build a compact linkage system (using any classes of levers) that will raise a weight, using only the materials available.

Design Criteria

- The linkage system must raise a 0.25-N weight a height of 20 cm.
- The system must include at least two levers.
- All parts of the system must stay within the size of a "box" 0.5 m long, 0.5 m wide, and 0.5 m high.

Materials

- 30 (drilled as needed) popsicle sticks
- glue
- apron
- 10 paper fasteners
- 0.25-N (25-g) mass
- thin rope or twine
- metre stick
- newton spring scale

Build

1 Using a detailed technical drawing, design a linkage system according to the above criteria. On your diagram, indicate materials, size, classes of lever, and how they will work. (3C) (6C)

2 With your teacher's approval, build the system according to your design. (5E)

(a) Does your linkage system fit within the size limits?

Test

3 Measure your system to ensure it meets the size limit.
- If it does not, redesign the system so it does.

4 Test your system to see if it raises the 0.25-N weight the minimum height.
- If your system does not pass the test, examine the system and consider how to redesign it.
- Redraw your diagram.
- Rebuild your linkage system, measure it, and test it until it works.

Evaluate

5 Evaluate your results by answering the following questions.

(a) What other materials might have made the linkage system easier to build?

(b) Which type of lever takes up more space, a Class 1 lever or a Class 2 lever?

(c) How could you improve the mechanical advantage of your system?

Figure 1

a An upright piano takes up much less floor space than a grand piano.

b To achieve this, its series of three levers are arranged in a compact space. The first lever is the piano key, which pushes a second lever, which in turn moves a third lever that strikes a string, producing a sound.

6 Using the spring scale, measure how much force is needed to raise the 0.25-N weight.

✎ (a) Record the effort force.

✎ (b) Calculate and record the mechanical advantage of your system.

7 Present your linkage system to the class, explaining your strategies during the design process, any problems you encountered, and your solutions to those problems. Present a diagram showing any improvements you could make to your system.

Design Challenge

Do you think that a multiple-lever system is a practical choice for your can crusher Challenge?

Making Connections

1. Levers are frequently used in sports.

   (a) Think of three sports in which a lever is the main tool that players use.

   (b) Where is the fulcrum on each lever?

   (c) Have the designs or materials changed in any of them over time? Why?

Reflecting

2. Technical drawings can be drawn from different views to show different parts of a system.

   6C (a) Draw the system of linked levers you designed from a different view.

   (b) Does this diagram help to illustrate any feature better than your first diagram did?

   (c) Why would different diagrams of the same product be important?

Simulating Human Movement

Figure 1
Robots can replace workers in dangerous places that may have high levels of radioactivity, poisonous fumes, or a high risk of infection.

Robots: Sophisticated Machines

Robots are one of the most important types of machines being used today. They are sophisticated systems that are controlled by computer and can replace humans in many different situations. Robots are the ideal replacement for certain jobs that need to be done in cold, hot, noisy, or dangerous places (**Figure 1**). They can even retrieve potentially explosive devices.

Most robots copy the movements of the human arm. (See **Figure 2**.) A robotic arm is a series of subsystems that, when combined, performs a specific task. Robotic arms use an electronic system to direct their movement, a hydraulic system to lift and move heavy things, and a mechanical system to grasp objects.

Because it is so difficult to copy all of a human arm's complicated movements, robots are most efficient at doing repetitive tasks such as assembly-line work. Instead of a hand, robots are often fitted with a drill, screwdriver, or spray gun, and can repeat the same task quickly and exactly, without the strain or injuries that humans often get through repetitive movements.

Although basic human arm movements can be copied, it is more difficult to build a robot that has the same delicate precision as human hands and fingers. This is because humans have an extremely sensitive sense of touch, which is controlled by the brain. Also, humans are helped by their sense of sight. Most robots lack any sensors and simply have a computer program that instructs levers where to move.

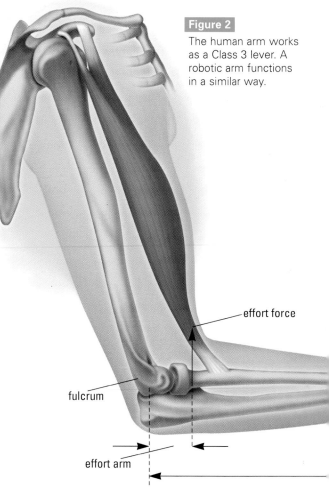

Figure 2

The human arm works as a Class 3 lever. A robotic arm functions in a similar way.

effort force

fulcrum

effort arm

The challenge is to build a robot with enough electronic sensors at its "fingertips" so that they will supply the robot's computer, or "brain," with detailed information about the type of object being handled (**Figure 3**).

Figure 3

Designers use hundreds of tiny electronic sensors in the robot's "fingers" so it can pick up an egg without crushing it.

Artificial Arms

In some ways an artificial arm is simpler than a robotic arm because the person operating the artificial arm "knows" what to do. But opening and closing an artificial hand still involves complicated computerization and mechanical design.

The most sophisticated models detect the tiny electronic signals transmitted through the human nervous system. This is done by connecting electrodes in the mechanical arm to the nerve endings on the person's arm. Wires then carry signals from the brain to motors in the arm, enabling the person to control the artificial hand (**Figure 4**).

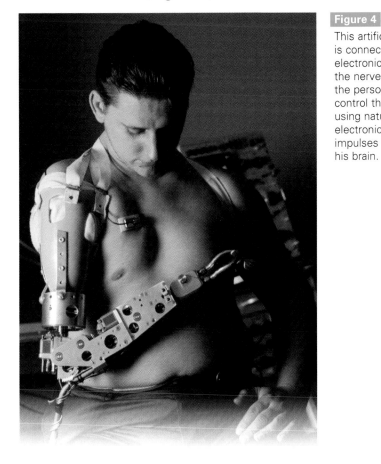

Figure 4

This artificial arm is connected electronically to the nerves so the person can control the arm using natural electronic impulses from his brain.

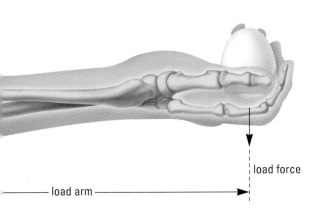

load force

load arm

SKILLS HANDBOOK: (8D) Exploring an Issue (8A) Writing a Report

Mechanical Advantage and Efficiency **17**

Understanding Concepts

1. **(a)** What part of the human body do most robots copy? Why?

   (b) What type of simple machine is this?

2. What aspect of humans is difficult to copy in a robot?

3. What types of jobs do robots do best? Explain.

Making Connections

4. In outer space, the Canadian-made Canadarm is a large, mechanized arm and "hand," operated by computer technology, that astronauts use to move objects outside the space shuttle.

   (a) What is the advantage of using the Canadarm instead of the astronauts themselves?

   (b) Are there disadvantages to using a robotic arm for work in outer space?

Exploring

5. Artificial intelligence refers to (8D) computers and robots that can "think" and "learn" like human beings. However, many scientists say that the human brain is impossible to copy because it is so complicated. Using the Internet or the library, find out more about artificial intelligence.

6. Industries are increasingly (8A) replacing humans with robots in work that is repetitive or dangerous. However, many argue that this takes jobs away from people who need them. Do you think robots are a good idea? Do some research to support your opinion.

Design Challenge

How can the simple design of most robots help in the design of your remote-control puppet?

Pulleys, Wheel and Axle, and Gears

Rotary motion is one of the most common types of motion found in machines. Many machines generate rotary motion that has to be transmitted from one place to another. This is accomplished by mechanisms that use pulleys, gears, and wheels. As with some levers, there is a mechanical advantage to these mechanisms that is greater than one. But there is a price to be paid—the effort force must move over a greater distance than the load force. Using mechanical advantage and velocity ratio, designers and engineers can choose the most effective mechanism for a particular machine.

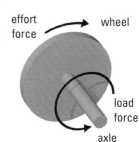

Figure 1

Is the MA of this wheel-and-axle machine greater than 1, equal to 1, or less than 1?

Wheel and Axle

The wheel and axle is the most common wheel mechanism. It consists of a large-diameter disk, (the wheel), which is attached to a small diameter shaft, (the axle). The effort force on the wheel (**Figure 1**) magnifies the load force on the axle. In the screwdriver (**Figure 2**), the handle is larger in diameter than the shaft. This means that a small force on the handle will create a large force on the shaft and thus on the screw. The steering wheel of a car performs the same function of magnifying the driver's force on the steering column. The larger the steering wheel, the more force the driver can send to the wheels.

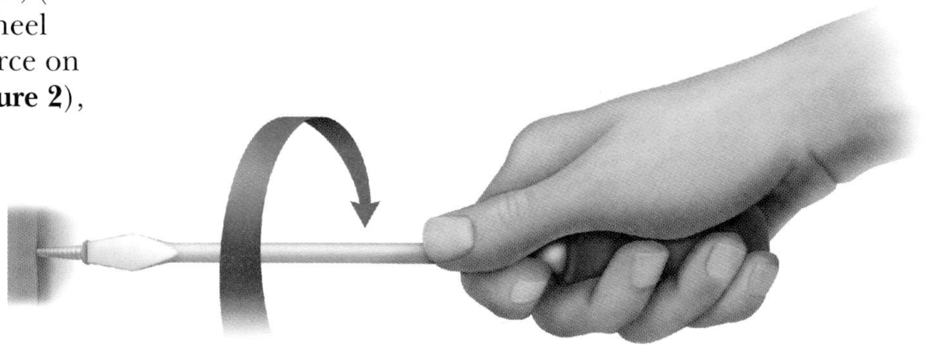

The wheel and axle can also work the opposite way. With a bicycle, a large effort force is applied to the axle to overcome the smaller load force acting on the rim of the wheel. The advantage is that the rim of the wheel must travel much farther than the axle in the same amount of time, enabling the bicycle to go very fast. Depending on the purpose of the machine, wheel-and-axle mechanisms can be designed to transfer rotary motion to rotary motion, rotary motion to linear motion (**Figure 3**), and linear motion to rotary motion.

Figure 2

Which part of the screwdriver is the wheel? Which part is the axle?

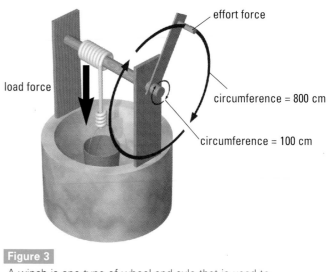

Figure 3

A winch is one type of wheel and axle that is used to move or lift a heavy weight. What is its velocity ratio?

Pulleys

Cranes or the rigging on a sailboat use sets of pulleys joined together by ropes and chains to lift heavy loads or exert large forces. A single pulley is a wheel-and-axle mechanism that is used to change the direction of a force or motion. There are two types of pulley systems: fixed and movable. The simplest system is the single fixed pulley. Its only function is to change the direction of the force. The other systems are designed to multiply the force (**Figure 4**).

The single fixed pulley has a mechanical advantage of only 1, so it is useful only when the object's volume is too large to be picked up by hand or when the space around it is limited. In the single movable pulley, however, half the load is supported by the rope where it is attached to the ceiling, while the other half of the load is supported by the free end of the rope **Figure 4b**. Thus, the effort force required is only one-half the load force. Therefore the mechanical advantage is 2.

A simple method for determining the mechanical advantage of a pulley system without friction is to count the lengths of rope between the pulleys that share the load. For example, in **Figure 4d**, the multiple pulley system shows 3 ropes sharing the load (they pull up). The rope being pulled down does not count since it doesn't support the load. Therefore the mechanical advantage is 3.

With a pulley system that has a MA greater than 1, a smaller effort force allows you to lift a larger load force. However, the effort force will have to move even a greater distance than the load force. This is the penalty you pay for gaining a mechanical advantage. The velocity ratio is:

$$\text{Velocity Ratio (VR)} = \frac{\text{distance moved by effort force}}{\text{distance moved by load force}}$$

The velocity ratio for the multiple fixed pulley in **Figure 4d** is also 3. To raise the weight 2 m, you must pull 6 m of rope through the pulley. In other words, each of the 3 rope lengths sharing the load must be shortened by 2 m to raise the load 2 m.

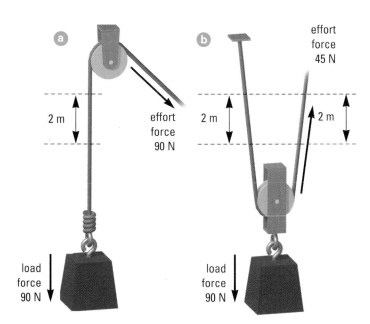

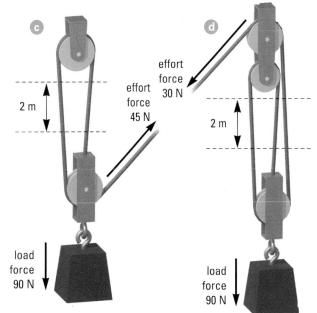

(a) Single fixed pulley. The force simply changes direction. The effort force is equal to the load force. By pulling in 2 m of rope, the weight will rise 2 m.

(b) Single movable pulley.

(c) Double fixed pulley. In this pulley 4 m of rope must be pulled to raise the mass 2 m.

(d) Multiple fixed pulley. The load force, 90 N, is shared by 3 lengths of rope. The effort force needed is 30 N, and 6 m of rope must be pulled in to raise the weight 2 m.

Gears

Gears are toothed wheels, usually made from metal or plastic, and used to speed up or slow down motion. A **gear train** consists of two wheels (or more) with meshed teeth (**Figure 5**).

Gears work by reducing the required revolving force (**Figure 5a**) or increasing it (**Figure 5b**). The ratio of the circumference of the gears, called the **gear ratio**, is similar to the velocity ratio on a pulley system. Since the teeth on meshing gears are the same distance apart, you can find the gear ratio by simply counting the number of teeth on each gear.

In some cases, like a bicycle (**Figure 6**), the gears turn separately and are joined by a chain. The pedal drives the front gear, and the chain transfers the turning force to the rear gear.

By using a variety of gear ratios on changing terrain, you can increase or decrease the turning force and even out the effort required. This makes you less tired.

Figure 5

The order of the gears in a gear train determines whether motion is speeded up or slowed down.

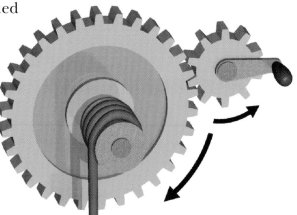

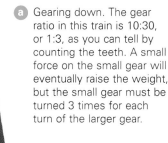

(a) Gearing down. The gear ratio in this train is 10:30, or 1:3, as you can tell by counting the teeth. A small force on the small gear will eventually raise the weight, but the small gear must be turned 3 times for each turn of the larger gear.

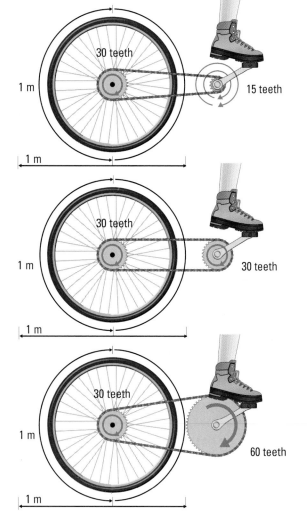

Figure 6

(a) When going up a steep hill against the force of gravity, it's harder to revolve the gear, so you should switch to a smaller front gear. With a low gear ratio, the gear can be turned with less force than before, but it must revolve farther around to cover the same distance as in (b).

$$\text{gear ratio} = \frac{15 \text{ teeth}}{30 \text{ teeth}}$$
$$= 1:2$$

bike covers 1 m with 2 revolutions of the front gear

(b) When a bike is pedalled on flat ground, and the gears are the same size, both the gears rotate at the same rate.

$$\text{gear ratio} = \frac{30 \text{ teeth}}{30 \text{ teeth}}$$
$$= 1:1$$

bike covers 1 m with 1 revolution of the front gear

(c) When going downhill, gravity helps to pull you downward, and it's easy to revolve the gears, so you should switch to a large front gear. With a high gear ratio, you need to push with more force than in (a), but with just a ½ revolution of the gear you cover the same distance.

$$\text{gear ratio} = \frac{60 \text{ teeth}}{30 \text{ teeth}}$$
$$= 2:1$$

bike travels 1 m with ½ revolution of the front gear

b Gearing up. The gear ratio in this train is 30:10, or 3:1. Turning the large gear will quickly raise the weight, as the small gear will turn three times faster than the large gear; however, arranging the gears in this way requires more force.

Design Challenge

How does the wheel and axle fit into your design of the windmill-operated water well?

Does the bicycle give you any ideas about how to transfer power from the windmill to the well?

Understanding Concepts

1. How does a pulley system achieve a mechanical advantage?

2. Calculate the mechanical advantage and velocity ratio for the single fixed pulley in **Figure 7** and for the single movable pulley in **Figure 8**.

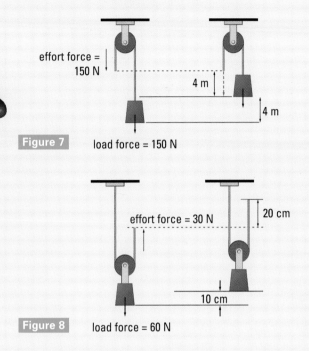

effort force = 150 N

4 m

4 m

Figure 7   load force = 150 N

effort force = 30 N

20 cm

10 cm

Figure 8   load force = 60 N

3. What does a gear ratio describe?

4. Ahman is trying to lift an 8-N load that is attached to a fixed 2-pulley system. His hands move a distance of 1.6 m, while the load moves 0.8 m. What force is required to lift the load?

Making Connections

5. If a wheel and axle has a mechanical advantage of 3, what effort force is required to move a load of 30 N?

6. Natasha has to pull in 25 m of rope to raise a 200-N weight 5 m using a pulley system.

   (a) What is the velocity ratio?

   (b) How much force does Natasha use to lift the weight?

7. Dave drives his jeep off a highway onto a steep, muddy uphill road. Does he need a higher or lower gear ratio?

Exploring

8. **(a)** What type of simple machine is a windmill?

   (b) Find out how a windmill works to grind grain.

   6C **(c)** Draw a simple diagram of its operation.

Mechanisms in Giant Machines

Even the largest, most complicated machines are formed from simple machines organized into mechanisms. Each mechanism has a function and, linked together, they all work to reduce strain on parts and lessen the amount of fuel required.

Giant Draglines

Dragline excavators (**Figure 1**) are some of the largest machines made. One common use is in open-pit coal mines, where they are used to remove the layers of soil and rock that cover the coal. They are also used to dig underwater, deepening channels for ships.

A dragline works by simply dropping an empty bucket on the ground from the tip of its crane. A winch is then used to drag the bucket, full of earth, along the ground. The loose, excavated earth that has been pulled in is then piled up so that trucks can remove it at a later time.

(a) Study **Figure 1**. What is the advantage of dragging the dirt instead of lifting it?

(b) What type of lever is the bucket attached to? Where is its fulcrum?

(c) Identify any pulley systems in this machine. What are their functions?

Figure 1

This dragline is one of the largest machines in the world. It operates in a coal mine in Ohio. The bucket on this dragline excavator is larger than a two-storey house and can hold more than a dozen cars.

Figure 2

Power shovels are used to scoop up loose earth or rock. A power shovel is much larger than most machines, and its bucket can hold one car. However, it's small compared to the dragline in Figure 1!

Giant Power Shovels

Power shovels are used to pick up broken-up earth or rock and load it into trucks (**Figure 2**). They may be used to help remove the dirt excavated by a dragline, or they may be used at large construction sites where earth is being removed for a foundation, or in open-pit mines to load mineral-containing rock into trucks.

(d) The bucket of a power shovel is smaller than that on a dragline. Why?

(e) What types of levers can you see in the power shovel? Where are their fulcrums?

(f) What is the function of the pulley system?

(g) Since the load in the bucket requires so much engine power, why don't the engineers include many more pulleys? (Hint: Consider the force acting between each cable and the surface of each pulley).

Understanding Concepts

1. Each of these large machines can be thought of as a system. For each machine, identify as many subsystems as you can. Give a function for each subsystem.

Making Connections

2. Giant machinery is increasingly being computerized so that the equipment operates smoothly within its designed limits. Explain how this can cut costs.

Exploring

3. Many smaller excavators used to dig foundations for houses have hydraulic systems that perform the digging and lifting motions of the shovel. Why do you think the giant machines are designed with pulleys for these functions instead of hydraulics?

Reflecting

4. Because giant machines such as excavators can work so efficiently, it has become cheaper to mine ore deposits that were not previously considered worthwhile. What environmental concerns must be considered as such machines get bigger and more efficient?

Moving Efficiently

Friction—we couldn't get along without it and yet we try hard to reduce it. **Friction** is the force that resists the movement of objects sliding or rolling over one another. It is created whenever surfaces move across each other. The smoother the surfaces, the less the friction. However, even the smoothest surfaces, such as paper, shiny metal, or plastic, have microscopic bumps on them that cause friction (**Figure 1**). As an object moves across these surfaces, the tiny bumps on the object and sliding surface collide, and force is required to move the bumps past each other.

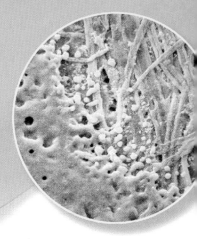

Figure 1

Paper looks and feels smooth, but through a microscope you can see that even the finest paper is rough enough to cause friction.

Friction Everywhere

Friction is the main cause of inefficiency in machines. As two parts in a mechanism rub together, they lose mechanical energy, which is transformed into thermal energy.

Friction occurs between any solid surfaces that are in contact, but it is also present when an object is moving through a fluid. The bright light of a meteor as it enters Earth's atmosphere is visible evidence of friction between a solid (the meteor) and a fluid (the gas of the atmosphere).

Boats are particularly inefficient because they sit partially submerged in water. Water is denser than air and causes more friction. Because they have to overcome frictional forces as they push through water, boats are slow and require much energy to move. Hovercraft overcome this problem by floating on a cushion of air over the water (**Figure 2**), with very little friction to slow them down.

Figure 2

The hovercraft moves over a low-friction cushion of compressed air by drawing in air from above the craft and forcing it underneath with large fans. This air is trapped beneath the boat by a flexible rubber skirt. Propellers on top move the boat forward, at speeds up to 120 km/h.

Reducing Friction

Friction reduces the efficiency of mechanisms and releases heat that can damage parts, so we often want to minimize its effects. One way is to reduce the surface areas that are in contact. Ball bearings—small steel spheres—achieve this. Both bicycles and skateboards use ball bearings between their wheels and axles (**Figure 3**).

Another way to reduce friction is to use a lubricant. Oil, grease, and graphite are all slippery substances that are used as lubricants. In a car engine, for instance, where pistons move up and down rapidly in their cylinders, the engine surfaces are bathed in a coating of oil. If there's not enough oil, the heat created by the friction of the metal parts rubbing directly against each other can quickly melt some surfaces, destroying the engine.

Positive Effects of Friction

Friction is also extremely useful. When we walk or run, the friction between our shoes and the ground gives us the "grip" to move. The grip on the sole of boots and shoes is important because it provides the security that allows us to travel safely over different types of surfaces. Sometimes friction can be a life saver: it allows a moving object to slow down or stop. Bicycles and cars rely on friction between the brakes and the wheels to slow them down.

Understanding Concepts

1. **(a)** What is friction?

   (b) What is the main reason for reducing friction?

2. How do ball bearings increase the efficiency of many machines?

Making Connections

3. Which parts of a bicycle are designed to increase friction? Decrease friction?

Exploring

4. From what you know about friction, if a car has good brakes, does that make it safe to drive fast on wet or icy roads? Why or why not?

5. **(6C)** Although hovercraft generate little friction when they move, they have a significant drawback: they are difficult to steer in windy conditions. Suggest, in a drawing, a mechanism that would help solve this problem.

Design Challenge

Do you need to consider reducing friction or overcoming gravity when building your puppet, water well, or can crusher?

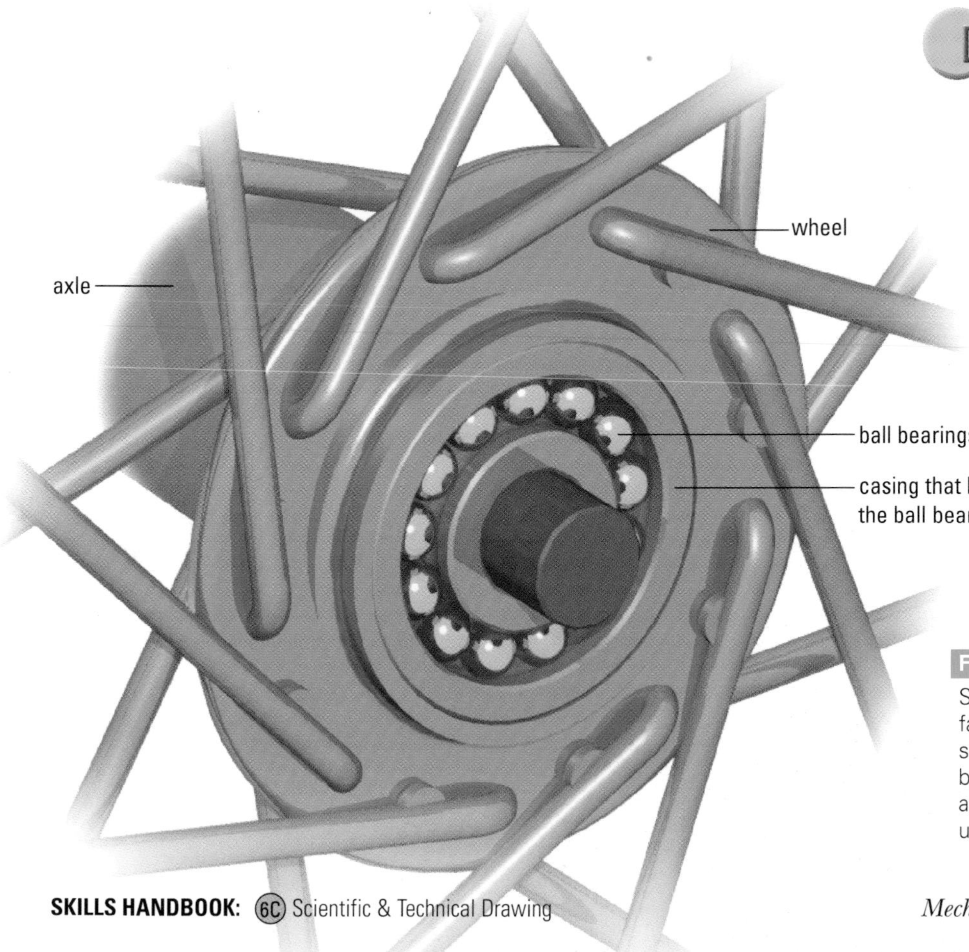

axle — wheel — ball bearings — casing that holds the ball bearings

Figure 3

Smooth metal balls called ball bearings create far less friction than two parts with large surface areas rubbing directly together. The ball bearings are contained in a casing attached to the wheel or the axle. They are usually packed in a lubricant, such as grease.

Friction and Mechanical Advantage

When we looked at the mechanical advantage of different mechanisms, we assumed that friction was zero. But in reality, all moving parts in machines experience friction. You've already learned that force must be exerted to overcome the friction between two surfaces before they will slide over each other.

Friction and Levers

With levers, friction is often low because the surfaces rubbing against each other at the fulcrum are small (**Figure 1**).

In **Figure 1**, 5 N of force is needed to overcome the friction at the fulcrum. Therefore, the effort force the girl needs to lift the boy is:

$$\text{effort force} = 250\ N + 5\ N$$
$$= 255\ N$$

The mechanical advantage is

Without Friction

$$MA = \frac{\text{load force}}{\text{effort force}}$$

$$= \frac{500\ N}{250\ N}$$

$$= 2$$

With Friction

$$MA = \frac{\text{load force}}{\text{effort force}}$$

$$= \frac{500\ N}{255\ N}$$

$$= 1.96$$

Friction and Pulleys

Rope that moves over even the smoothest pulleys still generates some friction. This means that extra effort force must be used to overcome the friction between the rope and each pulley. For example, three friends are driving on a small dirt road when a wheel gets caught in the ditch on the side and they can't get it out. The driver gets out her **block and tackle** (rope and pulley system) that she carries for such emergencies and rigs it up as shown in **Figure 2**.

To pull the jeep 3 m, they pull in 12 m of rope. The velocity ratio does not change because of friction:

$$\text{Velocity Ratio} = \frac{\text{distance effort force moves}}{\text{distance load force moves}}$$

$$= \frac{12\ m}{3\ m} = 4$$

However, the mechanical advantage is lower.

Without Friction

$$MA = \frac{\text{load force}}{\text{effort force}}$$

$$= \frac{3000\ N}{750\ N}$$

$$= 4$$

With Friction

$$MA = \frac{\text{load force}}{\text{effort force}}$$

$$= \frac{3000\ N}{900\ N}$$

$$= 3.3$$

The mechanical advantage is lower than it would have been because the group had to exert extra force to overcome the friction of the rope in the pulleys.

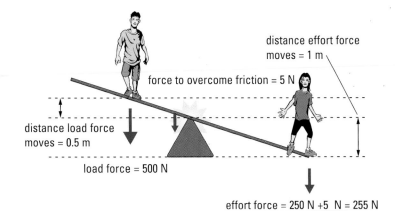

distance effort force moves = 1 m

force to overcome friction = 5 N

distance load force moves = 0.5 m

load force = 500 N

effort force = 250 N +5 N = 255 N

Figure 1

The seesaw's fulcrum consists of greased piping covered by a metal casing.

Figure 2

The group will pull in 4 times the length of rope needed to get the jeep back on the road. However, friction between the rope and pulleys makes the system less efficient.

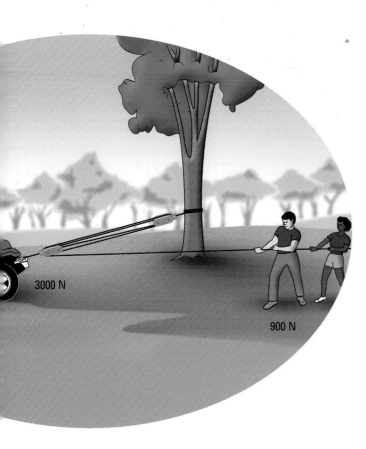

3000 N

900 N

How efficient was the system they designed?

$$\% \text{ Efficiency} = \frac{\text{Mechanical Advantage}}{\text{Velocity Ratio}} \times 100$$

$$= \frac{3.3}{4} = 82.5\%$$

Testing for Friction

Keeping friction to a minimum is an important way of having a machine work efficiently. However, when designing and building a machine or any simple device, it's impossible to predict exactly how much friction there will be between the moving surfaces without experimentation. The only way to find out is to actually measure the effort force needed to overcome the force of friction. If a new machine shows excessive friction, engineers and technicians may try to reduce the loss of efficiency by changing materials, polishing surfaces, or using a more effective lubricant.

Understanding Concepts

1. How does friction affect the efficiency of a system?

2. In each of the examples in **Figure 3**, calculate the mechanical advantage of the system without and then with friction.

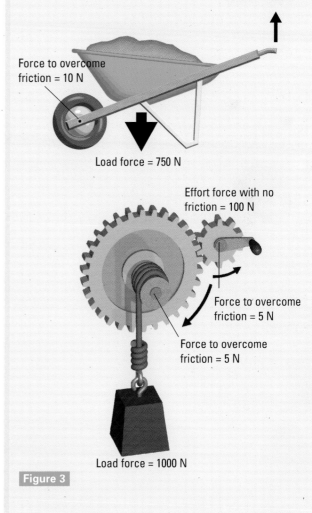

Effort force with no friction = 250 N

Force to overcome friction = 10 N

Load force = 750 N

Effort force with no friction = 100 N

Force to overcome friction = 5 N

Force to overcome friction = 5 N

Load force = 1000 N

Figure 3

3. Study **Figure 2**. How could the three friends improve the efficiency of their system? In the more efficient system, will the friends have to provide more or less effort force?

Design Challenge

The more moving parts a machine has, the more friction you can expect to find in the system. With the can crusher, you are trying to reduce the effort force needed to crush a can. What will you do to reduce the loss of efficiency due to friction?

Mechanical Advantage and Efficiency **27**

Moving the Couch

You have seen that mechanisms can be used in many situations to reduce the amount of force needed to move things. Pulleys are particularly useful because they are simple and they provide such a large mechanical advantage when lifting or moving heavy objects.

Problem

June wants to move a large couch (**Figure 1**) into a second-floor room in her new house, but it won't fit through the front door. She decides to rig a pulley system from the huge oak tree outside the house and bring the couch in through the large sliding doors onto the second-floor balcony. What type of pulley system will work?

Design Brief

Design and test a model pulley system that would allow June to raise the couch onto the second-floor balcony.

Design Criteria

- The model pulley system must be able to raise a 5-N weight a height of 0.5 m with a maximum effort force of 2 N, using only the materials available.
- Because June's rope is very short, the system must work using the least amount of rope necessary.

Materials

- 500-g mass to represent the couch
- 50-g masses, 4
- thin rope or twine
- 5 pulleys
- stand or horizontal rod to support pulley system

Build

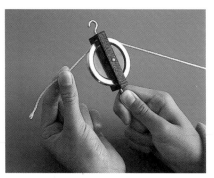

1 Use the equation for mechanical advantage to predict the approximate number of pulleys needed to raise the couch.
- Include a rough estimate for overcoming friction.

2 Draw a diagram of the set-up.

3 With your teacher's approval, build your pulley system.

Test

4 Place the weight on your system to represent the couch.
- Based on your calculations, place the weights on your pulley system that you think will raise the couch.

(a) Did the couch rise?

(b) If it did rise, is your pulley system using the least amount of rope necessary?

5 Redesign and test your pulley system until it meets both of the design criteria.

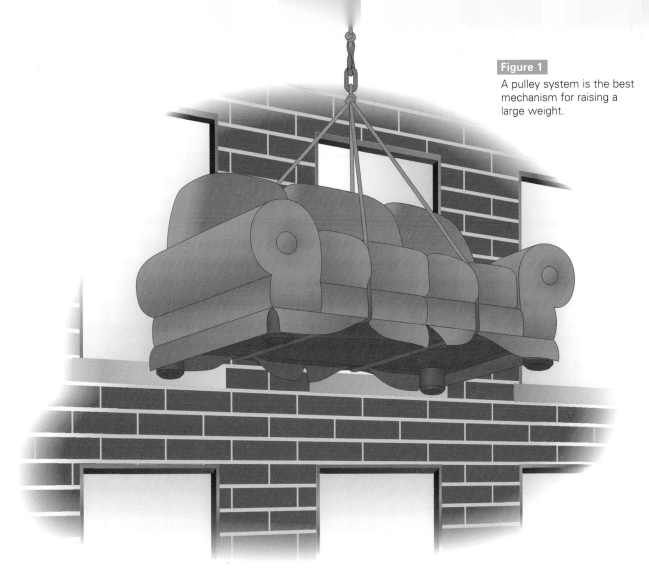

Figure 1
A pulley system is the best mechanism for raising a large weight.

Evaluate

6 Evaluate your results by answering the following questions.

(a) How many pulleys did your model system need to raise the couch?

(b) Did you need to redesign your pulley system before it worked? Explain why.

(c) How much force was needed to overcome friction? How does this compare with your initial prediction?

Design Challenge

In your design of the windmill-operated well or can crusher, you should include friction in your calculations. Where will the friction act?

Making Connections

1. When using a pulley system to lift an object, do you think it is easier to pull downward or upward? Explain.

2. What advice would you give to someone who is going to buy an expensive winch to help raise logs into position while building a small cabin?

Exploring

3. An engineering company that builds heavy equipment for the construction industry is planning to expand its research and design department because of many breakdowns of their equipment. Is this a good investment? Explain.

Testing Force and Endurance

Kim Parker says she wears many hats. A mechanical engineer working at the Bloorview MacMillan Centre's human movement laboratory, Kim is convinced she must be part designer and part engineer. The Bloorview is dedicated to helping children with disabilities and their families adapt to their special needs. She and the others at the lab design and test prosthetic limbs and components to make certain that the equipment the young people use helps them move and play better. To do this, everyone involved must be familiar with more than engineering. "In a lab like this in other countries, you would find engineers, physiotherapists, and kinesiology students working together," Kim says. "But here we have engineers who fulfil all those roles." This suits Kim fine. She enjoys the challenge of satisfying many requirements.

Kim has always had several interests. As a girl growing up in London, Ontario, she loved math and her Barbie dolls. Her father is a math teacher, and she thinks that might be part of the reason she enjoys it so much. Kim attended Queen's University and then the University of Toronto, where she earned her master's degree. For her thesis, she researched modifications of ankle-foot orthoses, which, she says, are "kind of like shoe insoles, only with kids, they wrap all the way up." Not surprisingly, her thesis work brought her to the Bloorview, where she has continued her testing. She enjoys her work and finds it very rewarding.

Doing such varied work in the human movement lab (or gait lab as it is also known) requires many different skills (**Figure 1**). According to Kim, sharpening your analytical abilities and using logic are the stepping stones. Add knowledge of mechanics, basic structure, physics of motion, a little bit about electricity, and a whole lot of math! On top of that, she must be familiar with the human anatomy particular to her area of study—legs—and computers.

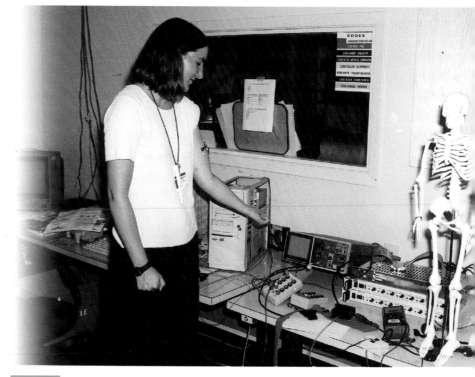

Figure 1

Engineers can use computers equipped with design model software to test a prototype structurally, and apply loads to different areas. In this way, they discover where the model might crack or break. Kim prefers a hands-on method. She starts with a solid structural analysis designed on paper, using her knowledge of the magnitude of force that will be applied. She then estimates where the critical high-stress areas in the design will be. Applying formulas, she can predict whether the design will work or fail if the stresses are beyond the material's capacity. Once this is complete, she builds a physical prototype. Using a jig and a pneumatic cylinder that is electronically controlled by a computer program, she tests the prosthesis or component mechanically. Always mindful of the key movements necessary for walking, she sets up levers to apply force onto the prototype (**Figure 2**). Finally, the prototype is tested on its intended user to measure its ability to help the person walk and to determine whether it is an improvement over the device already in use.

If a design doesn't improve a person's abilities or can't perform as well as the existing prosthesis, it goes back to the drawing board to iron out weaknesses and find new ways to solve its problems. Kim believes that these challenges make her job exciting because she is always experimenting with something different. New and better prostheses and components are being designed all the time. This aspect of engineering allows Kim and her co-workers the opportunity to see their designs make a real impact on peoples' everyday lives.

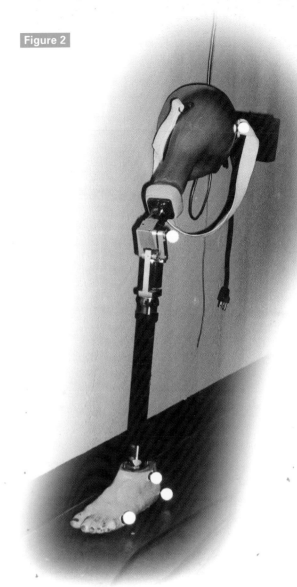

Figure 2

Try This — A Hand Model

A prosthetic hand is designed to perform many functions, including picking up small objects. An important consideration in the design of the hand is the length of the fingers.

Using popsicle sticks, thumbtacks, and elastic bands, set up the two "claws" as shown in **Figure 3**.

Compare the force required to squeeze the arms of the claws together.
Try to pick up a Ping-Pong ball with each claw by squeezing them.

1. How else could you change the force of each claw?

2. How could two claws with the same arm length have different amounts of force?

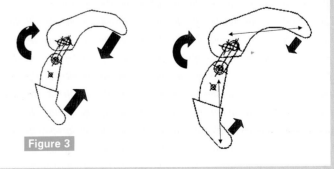

Figure 3

3.11 Inquiry Investigation

SKILLS MENU
- Questioning
- Hypothesizing
- Planning
- Conducting
- Recording
- Analyzing
- Communicating

Testing Shoes

Good sports shoes are designed to prevent injuries and are an indispensable part of an athlete's equipment. Runners require special features in their shoes because each running step exerts a large force on the body. When the foot hits the ground, the force travels through the foot, ankle, and through the bones of the leg, including the knee joint. Each foot lands with a force of impact that is several times greater than the force exerted by someone who is walking (**Figure 1**). Shoes for runners need to be designed to absorb a lot of the force of impact.

Not everyone is a runner, but we all put stress on our feet through standing, walking, and climbing stairs. The features of any shoe we wear should provide a cushion from the force of impact and provide "grip" with the surface (**Figure 2**). How can you test and compare the effectiveness of the absorption of impact and grip in two different types of shoes?

Question

2B **1** What question is being answered through this investigation?

Hypothesis

2C **2** Predict what you think the results of the two tests will be. Write a hypothesis explaining your prediction.

Experimental Design

3 Once you have read the two tests you will be conducting, write a detailed procedure considering the following:
- What are your independent and dependent variables for Test 1 and Test 2?
- What variables will you attempt to control in the two tests?
- Begin with an easy test that both shoes will pass. Then, make the test progressively harder until one shoe fails the test.

4 Create a table for recording your data.

5 Submit your written procedure and your table to your teacher for approval.

Materials
- 1 running shoe
- 1 street shoe or boot
- small plastic bags
- eggs
- newspaper
- board, 15 cm × 30 cm
- metre stick

Figure 2
In wet or icy weather, the treads and the type of rubber in the sole can mean the difference between safe and slippery running.

SKILLS HANDBOOK: **2B** Asking a Question **2C** Predicting and Hypothesizing

Procedure

6 Carry out your investigation.

Test 1: Comparing Shock Absorption

- For testing ability to absorb impact, use the egg in your test to represent a person's foot.
- Make sure that no components are loose when you carry out your tests.

Test 2: Comparing Grip

- Grip refers to a shoe's ability to prevent slipping. In your experiment, use the board at different angles to create a slope that will test the shoes' grip.

Analysis

7 Analyze your results by answering the following questions.

(a) Which shoe had the best shock absorption? The best grip?

(b) Do your results support your hypothesis?

(c) Do you think that the egg is a good model for a foot? Why or why not?

(d) Was your surface for measuring grip a good model for a typical running surface? Is this an important factor?

Making Connections

1. Why are the shoes you tested designed differently? Think of the needs of the person who buys the shoe.

Exploring

2. If you could use whatever equipment you wanted to measure the shoes' grip and ability to absorb impact, how would you set up the experiment? What factors would have to be the same for each test to ensure fairness?

3. Use electronic and print resources to research the key features in a good-quality athletic shoe. Draw a diagram of a "perfect" shoe and label the features. For each feature, write a description of its purpose. Summarize how each feature contributes to the product.

Reflecting

4. (a) If you could design your own ideal pair of walking shoes or boots, what features would they have?

   (b) What would they be made of, and how would they look?

   (c) Do you think others would buy your shoes if they were available?

Force, Area, and Pressure

Force and Pressure

A thumbtack (**Figure 1**) is a solid object. A force applied to one part of a solid—the head of the thumbtack—is transmitted directly through it to any other solid object it is in contact with—such as a bulletin board. But there's something special about the thumbtack's design that makes it so handy. As shown in **Figure 2**, we see that the force applied to the large surface area (the head of the thumbtack) is transmitted through the tiny pointed end.

The magnitude of the force applied by your thumb hasn't changed, but its distribution has. Instead of the force being spread out over a large area, the force becomes concentrated on the tiny surface area of the sharp point.

The distribution of force over an area is called **pressure**. This can be written as:

$$\text{Pressure} = \frac{\text{Force}}{\text{Area}}$$

The thumbtack works because it has two surface areas: the first one big, and the second one small. When the force is applied to the thumbtack on the large surface the pressure is low. At the point, because the force is distributed over the tiny surface area, the pressure becomes very high. The material of the bulletin board collapses under this pressure.

Figure 1

Thumbtacks are useful because they have surfaces that allow us to pierce things easily. How are they designed so that we don't have to use much force to make them work?

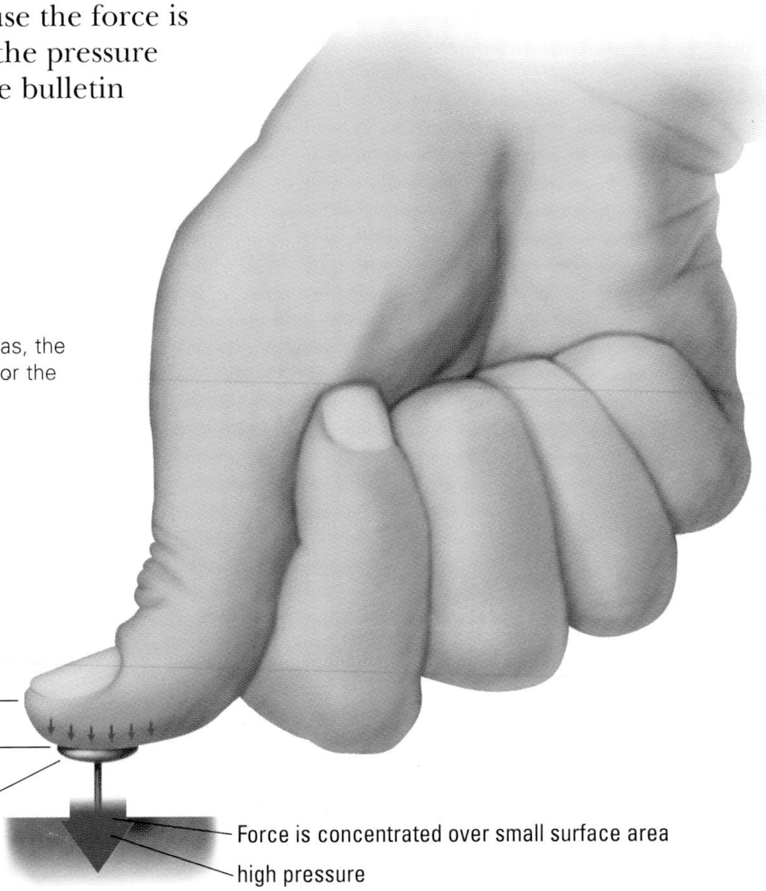

Figure 2

If there are 2 surface areas, the distribution of the force, or the pressure, changes.

The thumb exerts force onto the thumbtack

Force is distributed over large surface area

low pressure

Force is concentrated over small surface area

high pressure

Reducing Pressure

Snowshoes are also solids, but they work the opposite way from thumbtacks—they increase surface areas instead of reducing it.

If you walk in deep snow in your boots, the pressure from the boots will compress the snow and you will sink in. However, if you put on a pair of snowshoes, the pressure on the snow is lower and you can walk on the surface and sink only a little (**Figure 3**). The snowshoe reduces the pressure you exert on the snow because the snowshoe has a much larger surface area than the bottom of your boot. Because snowshoes distribute force in this way, they are a more efficient way to get across deep snow than regular boots.

Figure 3

Snowshoes lower the pressure on the snow and prevent the user from sinking in.

Calculating Pressure

As shown below, the equation for pressure is

$$\text{Pressure} = \frac{\text{Force}}{\text{Area}}$$

$$\text{or } P = \frac{F}{A}$$

Force is in units of newtons (N), and area is in units of square metres (m^2). Therefore, pressure is in units of N/m^2. One N/m^2 is also called 1 pascal (Pa). However, since 1 Pa is a very small amount of pressure, the kilopascal (kPa) is a more common unit: 1000 Pa = 1 kPa.

Suppose a student with a mass of 54 kg is walking on the snow (see **Figure 3**). When the student places all his or her weight on one foot, the pressure on the snow can be calculated as follows:

With Snowshoe

weight of student = 540 N

surface area of snowshoe = 0.20 m^2

$$P = \frac{F}{A}$$

$$= \frac{540 \text{ N}}{0.20 \text{ m}^2}$$

$$= 2700 \text{ N/m}^2 = 2.7 \text{ kPa}$$

With Boot

weight of student = 540 N

surface area of boot = 0.05 m^2

$$P = \frac{F}{A}$$

$$= \frac{540 \text{ N}}{0.05 \text{ m}^2}$$

$$= 10\,800 \text{ N/m}^2 = 10.8 \text{ kPa}$$

Design Challenge

How can the concept of transmitting force through a solid and either increasing or decreasing pressure apply to the design of your can crusher?

Understanding Concepts

1. Using your own words, define pressure.

2. Describe the main feature of an object that

   (a) increases pressure;

   (b) decreases pressure.

3. A pile of scrap metal with a weight of 20 000 N is dumped on a platform with an area of 25 m^2. What is the pressure on the platform?

Making Connections

4. Which would hurt more: a large man in running shoes who steps on your toe, or a small woman in high heels? Why?

5. A student going on a winter camping trip with her school will need to carry a heavy backpack. She decides to wear skis for the long trek instead of winter boots. Is this a good idea? Why or why not?

6. A person walking across a frozen lake accidentally breaks through the ice and falls in the water. Using what you know about pressure, explain how a rescue crew can reach the accident site, but not break through themselves.

Pressure on Liquids and Gases

In the previous section you learned that a force can be transmitted through a solid to create pressure. The force, however, is transmitted in only one direction—the direction of the applied force. Liquids and gases behave differently. Unlike the particles in solids, liquid and gas particles are not tightly bound to each other. Without a container to hold the gas or liquid, we cannot apply a force to them because the particles simply flow away (**Figure 1**).

A water bed demonstrates how a liquid in a closed container transmits a force. A force exerted on a liquid is distributed evenly to the entire inside surface area of the container. This principle, called **Pascal's law**, was discovered by Blaise Pascal, a seventeenth-century physicist, after whom the unit of pressure is named. Since Pressure = Force/Area, the pressure created by an external force is distributed over the inside surface area. Both liquids and gases behave in the same way (**Figure 2**).

Forces and Fluids

Have you ever noticed how much air you can pump into a bicycle tire? When you pump more air into a tire, the particles in the air move closer together; the air becomes compressed. Air and other gases can be **compressed** because in a gas there are large empty spaces between the particles that can be filled up (**Figure 3**).

If you ever try to pump more water into a full bottle, you'll soon discover an important difference between gases and liquids. In a liquid, the particles are already very close together, so they cannot be forced closer. Liquids are virtually incompressible.

This difference has an important effect on how gases and liquids in closed containers react to forces (**Figure 4**). If you press down on a liquid in a closed container, the liquid will not "give," because liquids do not compress. The volume of the liquid remains the same. However, if you press down on a gas, the gas will give. It will compress into a smaller volume.

Figure 2

When you press on a balloon, the force from your hand is transmitted evenly to the inside surface of the balloon

gas: large spaces between particles

liquid: very little space between particles

Figure 3

Gases can be compressed: you can add more particles to a gas, or force the gas into a smaller space. Liquids cannot be compressed.

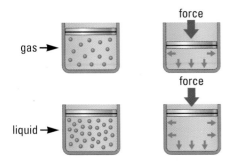

force

gas →

force

liquid →

Figure 4

When you apply a force to a gas, the gas will compress into a smaller volume. The pressure in a compressed gas is higher. Liquids cannot be compressed.

Figure 1
What happens when you press your foot down on an open surface of water?

Pressure and Temperature

Pressure in a container is caused by particles bouncing off the walls of the container. The more collisions there are with the walls, and the faster the particles are moving, the higher the pressure.

When you add thermal energy to a substance (increase its temperature), the particles of the substance move more rapidly. For a fluid in a container, the rapid movement causes an increase in pressure, because the faster-moving particles collide more energetically with the walls of the container. You've probably seen warnings not to heat cans that contain a gas. The reason is that the can might explode because of the rapid increase in internal pressure.

Using the same amount of thermal energy to raise the temperature of a liquid in a container will not result in as big an increase in pressure. That's because there are many more particles in the same volume of liquid: it takes a lot more thermal energy to make all of the particles move more quickly. Also, the particles in a liquid are less free—they are held to each other by attractive forces.

Pressure also increases when you compress a gas (put it in a smaller volume), as you can see in **Figure 5**. In the smaller space, the particles are more crowded together, and bounce off the walls more often. There is another effect of compressing a gas: its temperature increases. If you pump a lot of air into a tire, you'll notice that the valve and the tire get hotter. Some of the energy used to compress the gas is converted into thermal energy. Because liquids will not fit in a smaller space, you cannot increase the temperature of a liquid by exerting a force on its container.

Understanding Concepts

1. Why is a force transmitted differently in a solid than in a fluid?

2. What happens to the temperature when you apply a force to a liquid? a gas?

3. Look at **Figure 4**. Imagine that the pressure is the same in both containers before the force is applied. As the force is applied, the pressure in the gas container will become higher than the pressure in the liquid container. Explain why.

4. Explain, using your own words, what happens to a container full of gas as you heat it.

Making Connections

5. If you blow too much air into a balloon, it will quickly burst. Since gases are compressible, why does this occur?

6. To make a liquid change states to a gas, you add thermal energy. Explain what would happen in a container of liquid as the liquid is heated to its boiling point.

Exploring

7. There are several different designs of hand pumps for bicycle tires.
   (a) What is the purpose of each?
   (b) What are their advantages and disadvantages?

Figure 5

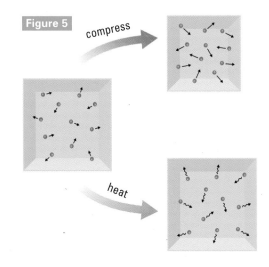

compress

heat

Mechanical Advantage and Efficiency **37**

Squeezing Liquids and Gases

You have already learned that applying a force to a liquid has predictable results. Gases can also be put under pressure, but they are different, because they are compressible. In this investigation you will compare how a liquid and a gas respond to the same amount of force.

Question
Do gases behave the same way as liquids when they are under pressure?

Hypothesis
2C **1** Create a hypothesis for this investigation.

Experimental Design
Using syringes, you will observe the effects of a force on a liquid (water) system, and then again on a gas (air) system.

2 Create a table like **Table 1** to record your data. Use "less than" "greater than" or "equal to" when recording your observations of the force required to raise the 200-g mass.

Materials
- apron
- goggles
- 20-mL plastic syringes, 2
- 50 cm clear plastic 6-mm tubing
- 4 clamps
- 2 support stands
- cardboard squares
- 200-g mass
- 5-mL plastic syringe
- 10-mL plastic syringe

Procedure   Part 1: Force in a Liquid System

3 Connect 2 20-mL syringes with plastic tubing.
- Remove the plunger from each syringe and fill the syringes with water.
- Put one plunger back in. Slowly push the plunger all the way down. Let the water run out of the other syringe.
- Put the plunger back in the second syringe and push it halfway down. The system should have no air in it.

4 Clamp each syringe to a support stand.
- Use cardboard to make two small platforms, large enough to support the 200-g mass. Tape a platform to the end of each plunger.
- Adjust the syringes so one syringe is fully down, and the other is up.

5 Place a 200-g mass on the platform of the plunger that is pushed down.
- Push the other plunger down. Feel how much force is required.
- Move the 200-g mass to the other platform. Push on the empty platform and feel how much force is required to raise the mass.

✎ (a) Record this system as the "standard force" in your table.

Figure 1
Truckers rely on closed air systems to operate their brakes.

Making Connections

1. When a liquid system is being used, similar to that in step 5, why is it important that it doesn't develop a leak?

2. Both liquid and gas systems are used in many types of machinery. When a gas system is used, as in **Figure 1**, what do you think is done with the gas first to make the system work efficiently?

Exploring

3. Design an experiment that investigates how applying the same force to liquid containers with different surface areas affects the pressure in the container. With your teacher's approval, carry it out.

Table 1

Fluid	Size of pushed syringe	Size of syringe supporting 200-g mass	Force required
water	20 mL	20 mL	standard
water	20 mL	20 mL	equal to standard
water	10 mL	20 mL	?
water	20 mL	10 mL	?

Part 2: Force in an Air System

6 Disconnect the system and repeat steps 3, 4, and 5 using several different combinations of syringes.

 (a) In your table, record the amount of force you use for each combination of syringes.

7 Investigate the same combinations of syringes using only air.
- When connecting syringes filled with air, make sure the *smaller* plunger is extended outward and the *larger* plunger is pushed down as far as it will go *before* you connect the tubing.
- Clamp the syringes as in steps 4 and 5.

 (a) Record the amount of force for each combination of syringes.

Analysis

8 Analyze your results by answering the following.

(a) What arrangement of syringes allowed you to raise the 200-g mass using the least force?

(b) Suppose you needed to raise a 200-g mass using even less force. How could you modify your system?

(c) Compare the plungers for the 5-mL, 10-mL, and 20-mL syringes. Using the relationship $P = F/A$, explain qualitatively your results for both water and air systems.

(d) Did this investigation support your hypothesis?

(e) Write a summary comparing a liquid system with an air system.

Pressure in Fluid Systems

When landing a big jet, the pilot lowers the plane's main wing flaps (**Figure 1**). The flaps must fight against the force caused by the air rushing by at 300 km/h or more, yet they lower smoothly and reliably. The system that operates the flaps uses liquids under pressure. An enclosed liquid that is used to transmit force is called a **hydraulic system**. Most hydraulic systems use an oil rather than water. Water is corrosive and is a poor lubricant.

You know how much force it takes to stop a bicycle in an emergency. Now imagine how much it takes to stop a fully loaded tractor-trailer travelling at 100 km/h. And yet that truck can be brought to a halt with a fairly light touch on a brake pedal. How does such a small force have such a great effect? Trucks use an enclosed gas system, a **pneumatic system**.

The advantage of hydraulic and pneumatic systems is that a small force can be used to lift or push very heavy things, over long or short distances, and with very little friction.

Figure 1
Many of the mechanical systems in an airplane use hydraulics to transmit forces, including the systems that raise and lower the landing gear and raise and lower the flaps on the wings.

The Hydraulic Press

You learned that a force exerted on a liquid in a closed container is transmitted equally in all directions to the inside surfaces of the container.

The hydraulic press shown in **Figure 2** illustrates an application of Pascal's law. It contains two **pistons**, metal cylinders that slide up and down inside a tube. As you can see, a small force can be magnified many times in a hydraulic system. The amount of force magnification is equal to how many times the area of the larger piston is greater than the area of the smaller piston.

Calculating the Mechanical Advantage of a Hydraulic System

We can calculate the mechanical advantage of the system in **Figure 2**. The effort force of 100 N is applied to the small piston. The resulting load force on the large piston is 2500 N.

$$\text{Mechanical Advantage} = \frac{\text{load force}}{\text{effort force}} = \frac{2500 \text{ N}}{100 \text{ N}} = 25$$

This system can lift objects that are 25 times heavier than the input or effort force.

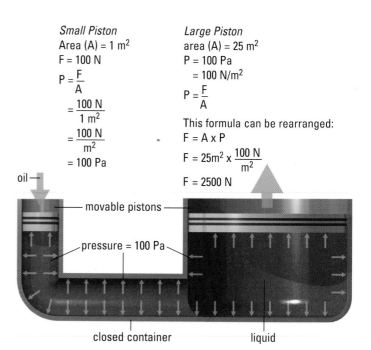

Small Piston
Area (A) = 1 m^2
F = 100 N
$P = \frac{F}{A}$
$\quad = \frac{100 \text{ N}}{1 \text{ m}^2}$
$\quad = \frac{100 \text{ N}}{\text{m}^2}$
$\quad = 100$ Pa

Large Piston
area (A) = 25 m^2
P = 100 Pa
$\quad = 100$ N/m^2
$P = \frac{F}{A}$

This formula can be rearranged:
F = A x P
$F = 25\text{m}^2 \times \frac{100 \text{ N}}{\text{m}^2}$
F = 2500 N

oil

movable pistons

pressure = 100 Pa

closed container   liquid

Figure 2
A force of 100 N is applied to the small piston in a hydraulic press. Note that the pressure is the same throughout the system (100 Pa), including at both pistons. However, the larger piston has a much larger area, so the force acting on the larger piston is much greater.

Cars and Hydraulics

By using different ratios of piston surface areas, hydraulic systems can create whatever multiplication of force is needed. A hydraulic car lift operates like the system in **Figure 2**, but with a much greater ratio of large to small pistons. A car's brake system also uses hydraulics (**Figure 3**).

Pneumatic Systems

Because pneumatic systems require pressurized gas to transmit force, they are connected to an electronically operated compressor, which greatly compresses the gas. The pressure of the compressed gas on the container's inside walls is very high, and a pneumatic system can generate a very large force. Large trucks, for example, use pneumatic brakes to apply a larger braking force than a hydraulic system could. Pneumatic systems have other advantages. Air is always available and in an inexhaustible supply, is less of a fire hazard, and is more environmentally friendly than hydraulic fluids. However, pneumatic systems require lots of room for the compressor, pressure boosters, and other components, and their complexity makes them more expensive. So, when there is minimum space and extra-large forces aren't needed, hydraulic systems are preferred.

Design Challenge

How can the pushing or lifting ability of hydraulic systems help in planning your hydraulic, remote-controlled puppet?

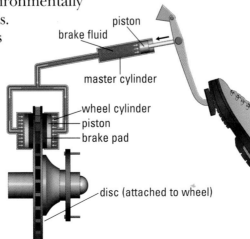

Figure 3

The foot exerts a small force which pushes a piston, transferring the force through the brake fluid in the master cylinder. This force places the brake fluid under pressure. The pressure is transferred to brake cylinders attached to each wheel. In the cylinders, pistons then push the brake pads against the brake disc with a much larger force.

piston
brake fluid
master cylinder
wheel cylinder
piston
brake pad
disc (attached to wheel)

A Hydraulic Solution for a Pain in the Neck

Almost all of us, young and old alike, are spending more and more time sitting in front of computers. But how we sit and look at the monitor is important (**Figure 1**), since poor posture often results in neck or back pain, or headaches. For the best posture, the monitor should be at the same height as your face. It should also be straight in front of you so that you're not twisting any part of your body.

Problem

In an elementary school, where many children of different heights use the computers, how can the heavy computer monitors be easily lifted to the proper height by a child who sits down to use it?

Design Brief

Design and build a model hydraulic system that can reliably lift a model monitor, using only the materials available.

Materials
- 50-mL syringes, 2
- 25-mL syringe
- 10-mL syringe
- 2 support stands
- 2 burette clamps
- narrow rubber tubing
- 1-kg mass

Figure 1

Design Criteria
- The hydraulic model must smoothly lift a weight of 10 N.
- The force used to lift the weight must be as small as possible.
- A technical drawing must show how the monitor is attached to the hydraulic system.
- A set of instructions must accompany the model, explaining why the device is there, when to use it, how to use it, and any safety precautions.

Build

1 Draw a complete diagram of the hydraulic system and computer system.

2 Build the system.

(a) How can you ensure that the monitor will rise smoothly?

Test

3 Put the 1-kg mass on your device and test it.

(a) Did the weight move up easily?

(b) How do you know that your design is using the smallest possible force, given the materials available?

4 If your system does not meet the criteria, analyze the system, redesign it, and test it again.

5 After writing your own instructions, including safety precautions, have a classmate use your system.

(a) Were any of your instructions unclear? Did you leave out anything? Modify your instructions as needed.

Evaluate

6 Evaluate your results by answering the following questions.

(a) Explain, using what you know about hydraulics and forces, why you chose the syringes that you did.

(b) Give two advantages of using a hydraulic system over another system in this situation.

(c) What part would you change to make this hydraulic system remote-controlled? Explain.

(d) Why is a clearly worded set of instructions important?

Making Connections

1. Referring back to your technical drawing, indicate where you could install a lever as a link with the hydraulic system to make it even easier to use. Explain your reasoning.

Exploring

2. Most products come with instruction manuals so that people can learn how to use them properly and safely. Instructions should be clear, thorough, and easy to follow.

(a) Find a manual for a product in your home.

(b) Are the instructions understandable and user-friendly? Give examples.

(c) Suggest some improvements for the instructions.

Design Challenge

How could this hydraulic system be used or modified for the design of the remote-control puppet?

What have you learned about instructions that will help you in putting together your own set of instructions for your Challenges?

A Student-Friendly Classroom

Your classroom and your living room at home look very different, from the floors to the furniture (**Figure 1**). Why are they so different? What factors do designers need to consider?

The most important reason for designing something is to solve a problem and satisfy a need. A successfully designed machine or product must function properly. But we have feelings and emotions. We do some things easily, others only with difficulty. We are influenced by the media and our surroundings. All of these factors must be considered in design.

Esthetics and Ergonomics

Esthetics relates to the qualities that make a design attractive. We appreciate these qualities through our five senses. Aesthetic factors such as texture, colour, and pattern are considered when designing products.

Ergonomics is the study of how to design objects so that people can use them safely, efficiently, and easily. For example, an ergonomically designed desk chair may provide back support for long periods of sitting. Designing products ergonomically means considering people's needs carefully, and analyzing how they will most likely use a product. Other ergonomic factors may include materials, durability, and health benefits.

Good designers consider many factors to try to meet the needs and expectations of consumers. Cost, of course, must also be considered. In this case study, you will design an ideal classroom based on ergonomics and esthetics.

Figure 1
Are classrooms a comfortable place for students?

Classroom Chairs

The most important design requirement for chairs is stability (see **Figure 2**). A chair must be symmetrical to balance properly. Classroom chairs have to be comfortable for students of many sizes, but they must also fit under desks. They must be strong to withstand years of use, but light enough for students to move easily. Finally, the cost of manufacturing the chairs should not be high.

(a) Examine your chair. Is it well-designed? Why or why not?

(b) How could your chair be improved? Consider specific factors, such as its shape, its materials, how it moves, its appearance, or any other features.

Figure 2
How well could you work sitting in such a chair?

Classroom Desks

Like classroom chairs, desks must be symmetrical for stability and balance. Desks should include space for storing schoolwork, and also comfortably accommodate students of different heights (**Figure 3**). Finally, the cost of making the desk must be reasonable.

(c) Look at your desk. Do you think it's well-designed? Why or why not?

(d) What improvements can you suggest for your desk? Consider factors such as work area, materials, height of the desk, storage space, or any other features. Ensure that each idea has ergonomic and esthetic benefits.

Figure 3

Desk size is limited by classroom size, but designers must ensure students have enough room to work.

The Ergonomic Classroom

A classroom should be spacious enough that students don't feel crowded and can enter and leave safely, especially in emergencies. The room must be well lit, with an efficient light source. Natural lighting from large windows is also beneficial and pleasant, and windows should be openable in warm weather. In addition to a blackboard at the front, bulletin boards or shelves on other walls can be useful.

(e) Examine your classroom. Do you think it is well-designed? Why or why not?

(f) What improvements would you make? Consider size, shape, colour, arrangement of furniture and work areas, and additional resources. Remember that cost is also a factor.

(g) Draw a floor plan for your redesigned classroom.

Design Challenge

What ergonomic factors should you consider in the design and operation of your remote-control puppet or can crusher?

Understanding Concepts

1. What does ergonomics refer to?

2. Why is ergonomic design important in the classroom?

Making Connections

3. What are the important ergonomic features of a baby crib?

4. Ergonomics are important when designing safety devices. When airbags were first introduced in vehicles, they were designed for an average-sized man. However, they proved to be dangerous for shorter women and children. Describe a testing process that would avoid such problems.

Exploring

5. Tools and simple, everyday items, from lawnmowers to light switches, are also designed ergonomically, both for safety and ease of use. At home, analyze an item for its ergonomic features.

   (a) Do you think these features are effective?

   (b) If not, how do you think they could be improved?

Designing for People with Special Needs

Products that are designed ergonomically for some people may not be well suited for others with different needs. Left-handed people find that scissors designed for the right hand don't work very well. Many people with special needs have difficulty using mechanisms not designed with their needs in mind. Modern technology combined with ergonomic design has created or modified many devices to help such people in their everyday lives (**Figure 1**).

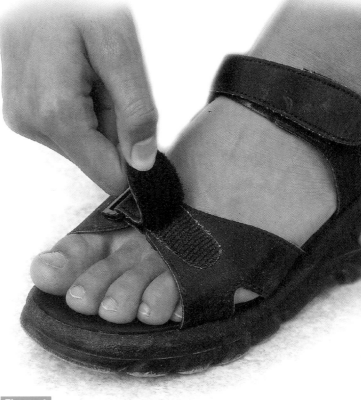

Figure 1

Not all designs involve complicated technology. Simple ideas, such as using Velcro instead of shoelaces, can be very useful for people with arthritis in their finger joints.

Modified Car Controls

Recall how hydraulics work in a car's braking system: a little force exerted by the foot on the brake pedal causes a large force to be exerted on the brake. This system can be modified for people who are paraplegic (paralyzed in the lower part of the body) or who cannot use their legs very well. In modified cars, a lever system is attached to the accelerator and brake pedals so that they can be conveniently and easily operated by hand. In this system, a combination of levers and hydraulics works well.

Designing Cars for Older People

What are the ergonomic needs of older people with stiff joints or worsening eyesight for seeing up-close? To understand how these problems can cause difficulties, ergonomic car designers wear special suits that restrict their movement at all of their joints (**Figure 2**). Back and neck braces further restrict their movement, and special goggles impair their vision. Applying what they have learned wearing this restrictive gear, the engineers have developed new car designs that include larger car doors, higher roofs, raised seats, and simpler, larger controls. These new designs are one way to help accommodate the changing needs of aging consumers and to continue to have a successful product.

Figure 2

By wearing restrictive clothing, a design engineer can feel what it's like for a person with stiff joints to get in and out of a car and operate its controls.

A Modified Sailboat

Sailboats have also been modified so that people who are paralyzed in their arms and legs (quadriplegics) can enjoy the excitement of sailing. A pneumatic system operated by a sailor's breath, called "sip and puff," allows the sailor to adjust both the sails and the steering of a sailboat (**Figure 3**). When the sailor blows into a straw and tube system, the force of his or her breath activates winches that unwind rope to let the sails out. Sucking causes a drop in pneumatic pressure, which reverses the winches and pulls the sails in. The quadriplegic sailor can also steer. By first biting the straw and then either blowing or sucking, the steering system is activated and he or she can turn the boat left or right.

Levers Are Easier

Levers provide another simple way of modifying items so that people can use them more easily. Doorknobs and taps on sinks are often modified with levers (**Figure 4**), since people with arthritic hands usually find knobs and taps difficult to turn.

Figure 3
This sailboat is designed so that it can be sailed using a pneumatic system that is activated by the breath of the sailor.

Figure 4
Levers need only a simple, easy motion to operate.

Design Challenge

How could you improve your Challenge design to better accommodate people with special needs?

Understanding Concepts

1. What is the main idea behind redesigning ordinary objects for people with special needs?

2. Why are levers often included in the design of objects for people who can't use their hands easily?

Making Connections

3. How might your ideal classroom from the previous section be improved to better serve people with special needs?

4. Many people use inventions designed to help with very common physical impairments, such as aids for hearing and sight. How are these products designed to make them more acceptable to people who use them?

Exploring

5. Many buildings are not well adapted or designed to provide easy access for physically challenged people.

   (a) Research ways buildings can be improved to suit their needs.

   (b) Design ways to make your school more
   8B user-friendly. Include technical drawings of any mechanical systems that are used.

Mountain Bike or Road Bike?

Cycling is becoming more and more popular. From leisurely riding on city bike paths to steep, boulder-filled descents down mountainsides, there is something for everyone. Such different riding conditions require different bike designs. Good ergonomic design involves careful consideration of how a product will be used. A bike that has been ergonomically designed for riding on flat pavement has very different features from those of a bike that is meant to be ridden offroad. Comparing the features of a typical mountain bike and road bike (**Figure 1**) can be helpful for the consumer trying to make an informed purchase.

Rugged vs. Light

One important difference between a mountain bike and a road bike is the design of their frames. Because a mountain bike is designed for rough riding on uneven dirt paths that may have obstacles such as rocks or logs, it is essential that the frame is durable and rugged. Durability means having a thick, heavy frame. Mountain bikes usually weigh several kilograms more than road bikes do. Because a road bike is designed for pavement, it is lighter and can go much faster. However, hitting even a small rock on a road bike can result in a dented wheel.

(a) Some bike frames are made of very lightweight, super-strong, expensive materials. Why aren't all bikes built this way?

Stable vs. Fast

Much-needed stability on a mountain bike means having lots of friction between the tires and the ground. When riding over round, wet boulders in a stream, or through mud, wide tires with a thick tread give lots of grip. In contrast, a road bike has thinner tires with less tread, reducing friction. Less friction means greater efficiency—less effort and more speed.

The handlebars, too, are designed differently. The straight, wider handlebars on a mountain bike give the rider more leverage to make quick turns around obstacles using little force. The narrower, down-curved handlebars of a road bike allow the rider to lean down and reduce wind resistance, which means less effort is needed to pedal.

(b) How are the tires and handlebars on a mountain bike better designed for going up and down steep hills?

Not All Hills Are Alike

Another difference is in the range of gear ratios available. Lower gear ratios help riders to keep moving when the terrain becomes difficult, as they can turn the pedals with less force and still make headway. The very lowest gears on a mountain bike allow the rider to pedal up steep or difficult terrain that would be impossible to climb on a road bike. Although road bikes often have as many as 18 gears, compared to 21 on mountain bikes, their range isn't as great, which restricts these bikes to steep but smooth, paved hills. Both bikes have comparable higher gears.

(c) If 21 gears are better than 18, why don't bike designers put that many gears on all bikes?

Speed Shift

How fast can you shift gears? On a mountain bike, very quickly. Just rotate the handlebars—front gears on the left, back gears on the right. If a cyclist comes around a bend and suddenly encounters a steep uphill climb, the gears on a mountain bike are placed ergonomically for quick shifting. On a road bike, changing gears takes a bit longer. It requires not only changing hand position to the levers located lower on the frame, but also riding momentarily with only one hand. This is fine on smooth, roads where you can see where you're going, but it's slow and awkward on trails.

(d) Some road bikes have gear shifts on straight handlebars, thicker tires, or other design features more like those of mountain bikes. Why would some consumers want such a mixture?

Understanding Concepts

1. Describe three features of road bikes that increase efficiency on paved roads.

2. Describe two features of mountain bikes that increase efficiency while going up steep dirt trails.

Making Connections

3. **(a)** Which bike has the best features for city cycling?

   (b) Can you think of a combination of features that would be safer and more efficient?

Exploring

4. Mountain bikes have more
   (8A) powerful brakes than road bikes because the former are heavier and riders often need to stop suddenly while going down steep slopes. Research how these special brakes work and create a report.

5. There are at least three different types of simple machines on a bicycle, in a variety of locations, and with different functions. How many can you find?

Reflecting

6. Bicycle helmets are required in some provinces in Canada but not in others. Some people think that this requirement will discourage people from riding. Should helmets be required? Why or why not?

Figure 1

Mountain bikes are designed with special features for riding on rough terrain. Road bikes have features specifically designed for efficient riding on pavement.

The Life of a Product

We live in a highly technological society. Our way of life, our standard of living, and the wealth of our country depend on the efficient manufacture and use of many different products. Although we usually think of efficiency in terms of how much effort is required to move something, efficiency also relates to efficient use of resources. North Americans are much less efficient users of resources than people in many other parts of the world. We are among the largest users of the Earth's resources and also create more garbage than almost everyone else. It's a vicious cycle. Because we throw away so much, we also use up more resources.

When creating a product, designers must consider not only a need or purpose to be satisfied but also the effect on people and the environment of the manufacturing process and the disposal of the product. How much pollution occurs while products are being made? How are products disposed of? Could alternative, longer-lasting products help us produce less pollution and garbage? Could some products be done away with entirely?

How can we become more efficient?

Metal: Stoves to Trucks

Iron is used more than any other metal in the world. This isn't surprising, when you consider that steel is made mostly of iron, with some carbon added. Steel is used in many places—reinforcing concrete in high-rises and bridges, and in vehicles, appliances, and computer parts. Scrap steel has become an important source of metal.

Recycling metal (**Figure 1**) slows the depletion of iron deposits and uses less energy than manufacturing new steel from raw materials. It also reduces the air and water pollution that results from the steel production process.

Figure 1

Once the metal scrap is sorted and graded, hydraulic shears and shredders are used to break it up. The metal is then squeezed into bales for steel makers, who rework it into coils or sheets for manufacturers.

Paper: Paper Towels to Drink Boxes

The use of chlorine in the manufacturing of paper products produces a serious amount of pollution. Chlorine bleaches the wood pulp so that items such as toilet paper and paper towels will be white (**Figure 2**). The use of chlorine creates highly toxic chemicals called organochlorines (carbon-containing molecules plus chlorine), which end up in the air and water systems. These poisons affect fish and wildlife at very low concentrations. Their effect on humans is not yet fully known.

Non-recyclable paper products such as diapers are also a problem, since they end up in landfill sites. To reduce this problem, reusable cloth or plastic products can replace disposable diapers, paper towels, or drink boxes.

Throwaway Plastics: Food Containers to Cameras

Plastic has drastically changed how we live in the past 60 years. It is used everywhere, from grocery bags to throwaway cameras. Plastic is handy because it is strong and durable. However, these same features cause problems when items are no longer needed.

Recycling plastic is only part of the answer. Recycling is expensive, and there are many types of plastic that must be separated before they are melted for reuse. Plastic is made from nonrenewable oil resources, but some plastic products are used for only a few minutes (**Figure 3**).

Figure 2
Should consumers demand non-bleached alternatives for products such as paper towels and coffee filters?

Figure 3
Plastic packaging made from oil, a nonrenewable resource, is a huge source of garbage. Buying loose fruit and vegetables can reduce inefficient use of materials.

Design Challenge

Consider the different types of materials you are using in your Design Challenge. Can they be recycled when they are no longer needed?

Understanding Concepts

1. How does the amount of garbage indicate inefficiency in the use of resources?

2. Name two benefits of recycling products made of steel.

3. What pollutant results from using chlorine to bleach paper products?

Making Connections

4. Make a list of plastic products at home that are used for a few hours at most.
   (a) Are all of these products necessary?
   (b) Suggest some longer-lasting or less wasteful alternatives.

Exploring

5. People continually buy faster and (8D) more sophisticated computers as they become available. But what happens to the old ones? Using the Internet and other sources, research recycling programs for old but usable computers.

Reflecting

6. Many products are wrapped in plastic. Suggest some reasons why. Are there alternatives?

7. Some manufacturers choose cheaper materials over the more expensive environmentally friendly ones. Do you think this reflects consumer preferences?

A World Without Cars?

Many people use cars to go to work, do their shopping, and travel on vacation. You may have gotten a ride to school. But use of these machines can conflict with other needs. (See **Figure 1**.) Are there more efficient products? What design factors should be considered when planning transportation systems?

Convenience vs. Danger

Cars are convenient, and allow people to travel comfortably in all kinds of weather. In rural areas with no public transportation, they may be the only way to get around quickly.

One drawback is that driving a car can be hazardous to your health. In Canada, approximately 5000 people are killed and approximately 200 000 are injured each year in car accidents.

In cities, pollution from car exhaust can affect people with respiratory diseases such as asthma. Also, the exhaust contributes to the pollution of the atmosphere, adding to global warming and acid precipitation.

Jobs vs. Materials

Making cars and trucks is one of the major industries in Canada. Factories employ thousands of people, from engineers to business people to assembly-line workers, while others are employed in selling and servicing cars and refining and selling gasoline.

However, the manufacturing of cars uses vast amounts of materials, including steel, aluminum, rubber, plastic, and glass. Many of these end up in car dumps. Used tires get piled into hills that occasionally catch fire, releasing poisonous fumes into the air.

Gasoline is a nonrenewable resource that comes from the world's oil deposits. Once we run out, we can't get any more.

Alternatives

Do we really need cars and trucks in cities? Can more efficient public transportation ease the congestion on city streets and reduce the need for cars?

Would more people walk or cycle on downtown streets if they were closed to vehicle traffic?

Figure 1

Cars can cause many problems, from traffic tie-ups to pollution.

 **Role Play** **Downtown: A Car-Free Zone?** (8D)

The municipal council of a large city is considering banning cars and trucks, except for emergency vehicles, from the one-square-kilometre downtown area. Traffic is congested during rush hour, and in summer, pollution can reach dangerous levels. However, many commuters feel that they need their cars to get to work, and some downtown store owners worry about losing business if people can't get to their stores by car.

The people listed below are part of a committee making recommendations to the city council regarding the proposed ban. Choose a role, write a report for the council, and be prepared to defend it in a municipal meeting.

The Roles

- A downtown resident whose respiratory disease is worsened by air pollution
- A suburban commuter without easy access to public transportation
- A downtown store owner who worries that the ban will discourage business
- A representative of a citizens' association that supports greater access to streets by pedestrians and cyclists
- An urban planner who wants to improve public transportation in the suburbs and create an attractive pedestrian environment downtown
- A traffic engineer who believes that the ban would cause even worse traffic tie-ups in other areas

How Would You Act?

- Choose a role, write a report, and prepare to defend your views.
- Which other players have similar opinions? Who will be harder to convince? Do you think their points are valid?
- To help support your position, look in newspapers, on the Internet, and at the library for information about cities that have had similar problems, as well as their solutions to those problems.

Design and Build a Mechanical Model or Device

Making a machine begins with an idea. Then technical drawings are created to show how the machine will work. Included with these drawings are calculations that estimate forces needed to push, pull, or lift. From these calculations, materials can be chosen and a final design created. Appropriate instructions are written describing how to operate the machine efficiently and safely.

1 A Can Crusher

Figure 1
More people would recycle if there was space for their cans.

Problem situation

Public recycling bins for cans fill up quickly because the cans are not crushed. The containers must be emptied often, and people simply throw their cans in the garbage when the recycling bins are full.

Design brief

- Design and build a wall-mounted can crusher that can be operated simply and safely.

Design criteria

- The force needed must be small enough that a child could operate the crusher.
- Technical drawings must show what the mechanical advantage of the crusher is, and how it will be achieved.
- The crusher must be able to crush many cans one at a time without requiring repair.
- It must be accompanied by simple instructions, including any safety precautions.

2 A Windmill-Operated Water Well

Figure 2
Can wind power drive farm machinery?

Problem situation

Many people who rely on a deep well for their water live in rural areas. It takes power to raise water from a well, and the wind is a cheap source of power.

Design brief

- Design and build a model windmill that will raise water to the surface of a well.

Design criteria

- An electrically operated fan at high speed, directed at the windmill, must be able to raise a weight of 0.5 N a height of 20 cm.
- The windmill must raise and lower the weight 10 times.
- It must be as efficient as possible.
- There must be an accompanying set of technical drawings and instructions, including safety precautions.

Figure 3
Puppets can provide hours of fun for small children.

3 | A Remote-Control Puppet

Problem situation

Young children want puppets that they can operate remotely so that they can set up a puppet show. However, they need a system that is easy to operate and rugged enough that it will endure rough use.

Design brief

- Design and build a mechanically operated puppet that is controlled hydraulically or pneumatically.

Design criteria

- The puppet must be operable from 2 m away.
- It must be easy to operate, with as little force as possible.
- It must withstand small children playing with the puppet and pulling at the different parts.
- Technical drawings and instructions must be included, along with any safety precautions.

Assessment

Your model or device will be assessed according to how well you:

Process
- understand the problem
- develop a safe plan
- choose and safely use appropriate materials, tools, and equipment
- test and record results
- evaluate your model, including suggestions for improvement

Communicate
- prepare a presentation
- use correct terms
- write clear descriptions of the steps you took in building and testing your model
- explain clearly how your model solves the problem
- make an accurate technical drawing for your model

Produce
- meet the design criteria with your model
- use your chosen materials effectively
- construct your model
- solve the identified problem

When preparing to build or test a design, have your plan approved by your teacher before you begin.

Unit 3 Summary

In this unit, you have learned that machines benefit us by making many tasks easier to perform. You have also learned to measure their efficiency and assess their environmental impact.

Reflecting

- Reflect on the ideas and questions presented in the Unit Overview and in the Getting Started. How can you connect what you have done and learned in this unit with those ideas and questions? (To review, check the sections indicated in this Summary.)
- Revise your answers to the Reflecting questions in ❶,❷,❸ and the questions you created in the Getting Started. How has your thinking changed?
- What new questions do you have? How will you answer them?

Understanding Concepts

- determine the mechanical advantage of various mechanical systems 3.2, 3.3, 3.8
- explain velocity ratio 3.2
- describe how pulleys, levers, and gears provide mechanical efficiency 3.2, 3.3, 3.5
- investigate and measure the force of friction 3.7, 3.8, 3.11
- describe the relationship between force, area, and pressure 3.12 ▶
- explain Pascal's law 3.13
- compare the effects of pressure on solids, liquids, and gases 3.12, 3.13, 3.14, 3.15
- explain how pressure is affected by temperature on liquids and gases 3.13 ▶

- explain how hydraulic and pneumatic ▲ devices help us 3.4, 3.6, 3.15, 3.16
- explain how a knowledge of levers aids in building artificial limbs 3.4, 3.10, 3.18

Applying Skills

- investigate how a linkage system can raise a weight 3.2, 3.3, 3.6, 3.9
- design, plan, and carry out the construction of a robotic arm 3.4
- describe how friction affects a machine's efficiency and suggest ways to reduce it 3.7, 3.8, 3.19 ▼

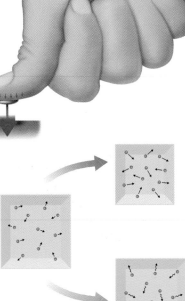

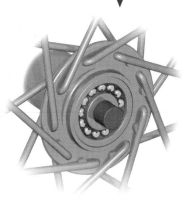

- design a mechanical system that is operated by hydraulic or pneumatic power 3.15, 3.16
- understand and use the following terms:

block and tackle	machine
compressed	mechanical
effort force	advantage
ergonomics	mechanism
esthetics	Pascal's law
friction	pistons
gear ratio	pneumatic system
gear train	pressure
hydraulic system	self-correcting
linkage	velocity ratio
load force	

- explain why gas ▲ under pressure in a container can be dangerous 3.13, 3.14
- explore the impact on the environment that results from the manufacture, use, and disposal of products 3.20, 3.21
- investigate the relationship between esthetics and ergonomics 3.17

Making Connections

- explain how the subsystems of a bicylce enable it to function 3.5, 3.19
- identify the kinds of information that help consumers make informed decisions when buying a product 3.11, 3.18, 3.19

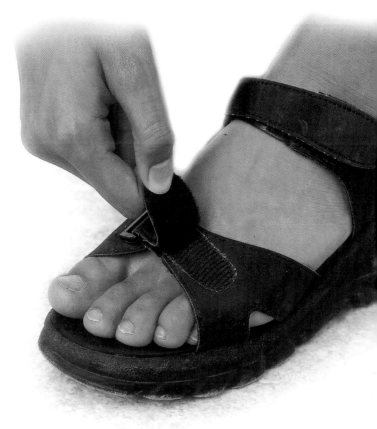

- assess the impact on the environment of the use and disposal of various products 3.20, 3.21
▼

- explain the use of ergonomics in designing functional products 3.17
- identify a career that uses modern technology to reproduce human movements 3.4, 3.10 ▶

Unit 3 Review

Understanding Concepts

1. List 3 ways in which machines can make things easier for us.

2. When a human operates a machine, he or she can adjust the amount of force depending upon the task. What features must a machine have in order to meet the requirements of a specific task when there is no human controlling it?

3. Classify each of the following as a Class 1, Class 2, or Class 3 lever.

   (a) broom
   (b) bottle opener
   (c) seesaw
   (d) fly swatter
   (e) nutcracker

   For each one, draw a rough sketch in your notebook and label the load force, effort force, and fulcrum.

4. How is a pulley a Class 1 lever? Explain.

5. What are some of the benefits of friction? Describe a situation where friction is necessary.

6. Explain how we can reduce friction. Why is it important to be able to control friction?

7. Compare the different types of pulleys. What are the different features of a single fixed pulley, a single movable pulley, and a multiple pulley system?

8. Describe the difference between mechanical advantage and velocity ratio. What does each type of calculation represent?

9. Write the equation for calculating pressure. How does increasing the surface area that an object covers change the pressure?

10. Explain the different effects that applying pressure can have on a liquid or a gas. Use the terms compression, particles, and temperature in your explanation.

11. Why do aerosol cans contain warnings not be left near a stove?

12. Outline the advantages of using either a hydraulic or a pneumatic system. When is one system preferable to the other?

13. Compare the different effects on the pressure applied to car brakes using either a gas or a liquid.

14. List some of the benefits of using recycled products. Give at least three specific examples and show how they help the environment.

15. What factors would help you determine how an office chair or desk should be designed?

16. List 3 plastic products or containers you use. Are there ways which you could avoid using them? What would be the benefit of using an alternate material or product?

Applying Skills

17. What would be the mechanical advantage of a lever that can lift 80 N with an effort of only 20 N?

18. In order to lift a load a distance of 6 m by a pulley, it is necessary to move the effort load by 3 m. What would be the velocity ratio?

19. In the gear mechanism in **Figure 1**, calculate the gear ratio if A is the gear being driven. How many rotations would be required for one complete rotation of B? Repeat your answer if B is the gear being driven.

Figure 1

20. A single movable pulley is being used to lift a 135-N object by using 75 N of effort. There is also an allowance of 5 N for friction in the pulley. Will it work? Why or why not? Would it work with a single fixed pulley?

21. Describe how an elevator uses a pulley system. Draw a diagram, labelling the load force, effort force, and fulcrum.

22. You use a single movable pulley to lift an object weighing 1000 N. You apply an effort of exactly 500 N. Will the object lift?

23. A wheel and axle system has a mechanical advantage of 4. The effort used is 12 N. Without accounting for friction, what is the maximum load force that can be moved?

24. How much pressure would be placed on a surface with an area of 2 m² if an object weighing 500 N were sitting on it?

25. A surface, measuring 0.2 m by 0.5 m, can withstand 2.5 kPa of pressure. What is the heaviest weight, in newtons, that can be placed upon the surface?

26. Match the following terms in **Table 1** with the correct descriptions:

Table 1

Term	Description
1. Compression	A The amount of space an object fills
2. Mechanical Advantage	B An object that is moved by a machine
3. Volume	C Speed at which an object moves in a given direction
4. Mechanism	D Squeezing together gas particles to fill a smaller volume
5. Hydraulics	E The number of times a machine increases or decreases an effort force
6. Velocity	F Forces are transferred in fluids in all directions
7. Load force	G A system of moving parts that changes an input motion to an output motion
8. Pascal's law	H A pressure system using liquid

27. Design an experiment comparing the efficiency of a hydraulic and a pneumatic system.

28. Mountain bikes and road bikes are designed differently. Complete **Table 2** indicating the differences and the reasons for them.

Table 2

Bicycle Part	Mountain Bike	Road Bike	Why?
Handlebars	Straight	Curved	Leverage on Road
?	?	?	?

29. How does a blender combine simple machines, such as a wheel, axle, and lever, to form a mechanism that makes work easier?

30. "A machine that requires more effort to lift an object than the load itself is useless." Explain why you think this statement is true or false.

31. How have robots, using a combination of simple machines, become useful in industry?

32. Use print media or the Internet to research prostheses. How have levers and other important machines become important for their design?

33. A new car factory is being built. The owners must decide whether to use people or robots at different points on the assembly line. Give some advantages and disadvantages of each to help them make a decision.

34. While building a high-rise apartment building, workers often perform much of the construction on the ground that will eventually end up near the top of the building (**Figure 2**). How do pulleys allow workers to do this?

Figure 2

35. In the mid-1990s, Toronto began building a new subway tunnel. A giant machine was used to bore the tunnel. Which mechanisms do you think would be part of this machine?

36. While driving at night, a motorist notices smoke coming from the engine of his car. The light indicating low oil is on inside the car. Explain what could be causing the smoke.

37. During rainstorms, drivers on wet roads are told to use extra caution (**Figure 3**). Describe, scientifically, why this warning is necessary.

SLIPPERY
WHEN WET
OR FROSTY

Figure 3

38. A commonly used magician's trick is to lie down on a bed of many nails. It looks quite dangerous, but the magician never gets poked. Apply what you know about pressure, force, and area to explain why this is so. What would happen if the magician lay down on only a few nails?

39. A nail is hammered into a wall, then a picture is hung on the nail. Describe the transfers of pressure involved in this process. Why is it sometimes necessary to use two nails?

40. You have been commissioned to design the layout for a new classroom.

  (a) Your task includes ergonomic designs for the chairs and desks, along with explanations for why they look the way they do.

  (b) Design special features that would make the room and equipment suitable for someone in a wheelchair.

41. An automobile manufacturer is designing seats for a new car model (**Figure 4**).

  (a) What are some of the design and ergonomic considerations that must be considered?

  (b) Identify some of the concerns that a consumer will have when examining the seat. How will she decide if the car seat is acceptable?

Figure 5

Figure 4

42. Playground equipment is designed with ergonomic considerations in mind (See **Figure 5**). For example, the type of slide may vary depending upon the age of the children using the slide. Design one for children 8–10 years old and one for children 5–7 years old. Consider the materials, shape, and height of the slide, as well as any other considerations you think are appropriate. Draw the two slides next to each other.

43. Your drink at lunch today could come in a plastic, paper, or metal container. What would be the advantages or disadvantages of each type?

Glossary

B

block and tackle: a rope and pulley system used to move objects

C

compressed: pressed into less volume or smaller space

E

effort force: the push or pull (force) required to move an object

ergonomics: the study of designing products intended to maximize safety, efficiency, and ease

esthetics: the qualities, such as texture, colour, and pattern, that make a product attractive

F

friction: the force that resists the movement of one object or surface moving across another

G

gear ratio: the relationship between the circumferences of the gears; determined by counting the number of teeth on each gear

gear train: two or more wheels with meshed teeth used to speed up or slow down motion

H

hydraulic system: a confined system that uses a liquid under pressure to operate

L

linkage: a connection of two or more levers used to transmit force and motion

load force: the force exerted by the load

M

machine: a device that makes work easier to do; a machine can transform energy, change the direction of a force, transfer a force from one location to another, change the magnitude of a force, and/or increase or decrease speed

mechanical advantage: the amount that a machine multiplies a force, measured by dividing the load force by the effort force

mechanism: a system of moving parts that changes an input motion and force into a desired output motion and force

P

Pascal's law: the principle that an external force exerted on a confined fluid is distributed evenly in all directions inside the surface area of the container

piston: a cylinder or disk inside a larger cylinder that moves under fluid pressure

pneumatic system: a confined, pressurized system that uses moving air or other gases

pressure: a measure of the distribution of force over a given area; written as

$$\text{Pressure} = \frac{\text{Force}}{\text{Area}}$$

S

self-correcting: able to adjust to a situation automatically

V

velocity ratio: the relationship between the distance that an effort force moves and the distance that a load force moves; written as

$$\text{Velocity Ratio} = \frac{\text{distance effort force moves}}{\text{distance load force moves}}$$

Index